PORTALS
TO THE PAST

The Story of Archaeology

PORTALS TO THE PAST

The Story of Archaeology

KATHERINE B. SHIPPEN

Illustrated by MEL SILVERMAN

NEW YORK
THE VIKING PRESS

TM
913
S557

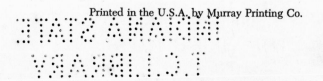

Like to the leaves of the forest,
So are the generations of men;
The wind casts the leaves to the earth,
But the budding woods shoot forth others in turn,
When spring brings revival of life.

So is the race of man;
It grows and then disappears. . . .

BOOK VI, THE ILIAD OF HOMER

Contents

Part I : Discovery

Part II: The Search for Understanding

Part I

Discovery

I.

The Long Search

This is the story of a long, unfinished search — the story of man's search for his own past. History to be sure is a record of the past, but history can tell only a small part of it. Men lived on the earth for thousands of years before history began, and even in early historic times there were many events of which no record was made; many things happened of which there are no accounts.

Instead of relying on written records, therefore, the archaeologists who carry on this search seek to understand how men lived and what they did, by unearthing and studying the objects they left behind them — their weapons and their jewelry, their tools, their dwelling houses, their temples

13

and their tombs. For material things remain long after the men who made them have disappeared.

It is said that King Nabonidus, who reigned in Babylon twenty-five hundred years ago, was the first man to be interested in the generations that had gone before him. He found some ancient ruined temples in his kingdom and had them dug up and restored. This may be true, but all the details of his work have been lost.

Apparently no one in Europe took much interest in what they called "antiquities" until the fourteenth century. Then the poet Petrarch paid a visit to Rome and was impressed by the beauty of the ancient structures he saw there.

Rome at that time was undergoing a process of rebuilding, much as some modern cities are today. There the ancient temples, baths, and other buildings were being torn down to make way for splendid, new Christian buildings, and Petrarch was horrified by what he saw. Pagan statues were being broken to bits, old coins melted for their gold and silver, gracefully carved columns stripped from old temples to decorate new churches, delicately wrought marble slabs burned to make lime for the new buildings.

Petrarch tried to persuade the Pope to stop this destruction. He even made a kind of archaeological plan, though no one had thought of archaeology in those days. The ruins ought to be compared carefully with the descriptions of classic buildings described by the old Roman writers, he said; the old coins should be studied and classified, the crumbling statues dug from their heaps of rubble, cleaned, and preserved. The radiant beauty of the Eternal City ought to be brought back to life.

People paid very little attention to Petrarch's ideas, and his preachments were almost forgotten when nearly a century later a man named Poggio began to talk about these same things.

Gian Francesco Poggio Bracciolini — or Poggio, as he was called — was a tireless and rather boastful man. He went about comparing the testimony of the old ruins with that set down by the Roman writers Livy and Vitruvius, and after a time, he made a catalogue of all the ancient buildings then standing in Rome. His attitude toward these old ruins was quite proprietary: because he had studied them so fully, he came to regard them as almost his own. He loved to take visitors to see them and to watch the newcomers' astonishment when they saw the grandeur of the crumbling vaults and walls.

Not content with his work in the city of Rome, Poggio was soon traveling by donkey-back to rummage for antique treasures in other parts of Italy. People watched him go from place to place, digging here and there, copying inscriptions, and loading himself down with ancient objects. Some were inclined to laugh at him, but others said he was an impostor who made forgeries of the things he claimed to have found.

"Where are you going?" they asked him. "Why do you spend your time in all this searching and traveling?" And Poggio, with a flair for picturesque language, summed up his purpose by saying, "I go to wake the dead."

In time the feeling for Rome's glorious past grew stronger. In every part of the city — at the street corners and in the little shops, along the waterfront and in the great palaces, everywhere — people talked of her ancient grandeur. To bring that grandeur back to life was now the ambition of rich and poor alike.

For a long time the popes tried to combat this feeling; in fact, they were among the chief destroyers of the ancient relics. One of them took stones from the Colosseum to build himself a palace, while another pulled down the circular temple of Hercules and destroyed the oldest stone bridge across the Tiber, to make cannon balls. Pope Innocent VIII ordered his architects to take whatever ancient building materials they wanted for erecting new buildings. Sculptured bas-reliefs and carved inscriptions were not spared: the hands of the stonecutters were ruthless in their destruction.

Gradually, however, respect for the relics of the past penetrated the Vatican, and the popes began to see beauty in the ancient objects. They built structures to house the treasures they found, and these were the first museums.

Gradually more and more treasures were brought to these museums — beautiful bas-reliefs delicately carved in marble, ancient inscriptions that had been unread for centuries. With greater frequency now news was brought of old sculptured figures found in the newly turned earth of some vineyard, or dug up by some farmer's plow. In 1506 the great piece of sculpture called "Laocoön" was discovered in the country outside Rome, and a number of people walked out to watch as it was drawn from the earth. Among them was Michelangelo, himself an artist and sculptor.

It is not hard to imagine Michelangelo's excitement when he first saw the huge figure of the father and his two sons struggling in the coils of the serpent. Pope Julius offered the farmer who found the "Laocoön" six hundred golden florins for it, and later it was brought to the Vatican to occupy a prominent place in the Museum of Pius Clementine.

Now, one after another, the sculptured figures which are still familiar and beloved today were dug from the earth and carried to the Vatican to be preserved and admired. The lovely figure of a young boy drawing a thorn from his foot was found, another of a lion clinging to a horse, a bronze Hercules, the urn of Aggrippina, the statue of the sleeping Ariadne, and many more.

There was much excitement in Rome as the old treasures were uncovered. But the discovery was haphazard. A peasant plowing a field might come upon a marble head or arm; a countryman might find a precious vase, filled with coins, in a dooryard; but other objects, equally precious, might be lying nearby undiscovered. Discovery and destruction went forward hand in hand. Glass and pottery often were broken in careless digging, and fragments of statuary that might have been saved and pieced together were thrown away.

In the sixteenth century Pope Leo X appointed the painter Raphael inspector of all the excavations in Rome and for ten miles around the city. Raphael then made a map of Rome, marking on it every antique structure that was standing in his day. On this map he divided the city into fourteen separate districts and urged the Pope to have each district studied by scholars grounded in the classics.

But Raphael died soon after that, and the Pope was interested in other things. So the systematic work he had urged was abandoned. Instead, collectors of antiquities were content merely to admire the beauty of whatever objects they found. Their wonder and excitement were summed up by the artist Albrecht Dürer, who, when he saw the designs on some coins that had been brought from Mexico, exclaimed, "I have never seen in all my days what so rejoiced my heart as these things!"

The spirit of wonder animated all the early collectors — wonder at the grandeur of the stone statues they labored to bring home from Egypt, wonder at the extraordinary winged lions and winged bulls they found in Mesopotamia, wonder at the gold of Troy and Mycenae, and at the vast palaces of the Sea Kings of Crete.

Only very gradually was this spirit of wonder changed to a spirit of scientific inquiry. For in the nineteenth century the spirit of science was invading every field, and archaeologists were becoming scientists, too.

Certain far-seeing men were leaders in the gradual movement that turned archaeology from a treasure hunt into a systematic and scientific search. The first of them was the English General Augustus Henry Pitt-Rivers, who inherited a vast fortune in 1880 and decided to devote it to digging up the barrows and earthworks on his estate in Wiltshire. He prepared for his work as if he were preparing for a military siege, so it is said, and thus laid the foundations for the advanced archaeological methods that are in use today. Half a century later Flinders Petrie, also an Englishman, again demonstrated the importance of precise method through his work in Egypt. After that one devoted worker after another followed their examples, until today the work of all archaeologists is carried on according to the same standard procedures.

How do they work? Their first task is to find the site where they will dig. This may be done by studying old records, by listening to talk of local traditions, or by examining the contour of the land, sometimes from the ground or, more recently, from an airplane. Recently, too, geophysical instruments have helped to pinpoint the best place to start digging, and electronic echo-sounding equipment has been successfully used, especially in underwater archaeology.

Once the site has been determined, trenches must be dug with great care and precision so that any objects found may be taken from their places with as little destruction of their surroundings as possible.

Finding the objects of his search is only the beginning of the archaeologist's work. Often he must treat the things he finds with chemicals so that they will not disintegrate upon exposure to the air. And he must make a record of every tiny fragment he has found, pack it with the utmost care, and interpret its meaning.

To perform these various tasks, the archaeologist must depend on the work of many other men. He must depend on the work of historians and scholars to help him to become familiar with the general setting and background of the things he is seeking. Scholars may help him to interpret unknown languages, too. Geologists, physicists, chemists, botanists — all must help him in their own separate ways. Even engineers must help him, for example, with such a gigantic task as sawing out a section of mountain containing the huge rock temple at Abu-Simbel in Egypt and hoisting it up to prevent it from being submerged by the flood waters that the building of the Aswan Dam will cause.

But following the established modern methods of excavating and getting the help of other men of science are only a part of the archaeologist's task. He must adapt himself to life in primitive and far-off places, for his work is often done in distant corners of the world. He must face the dust and heat of the Middle East, the jungles of tropical Africa, and the cold at the edge of the Arctic Ocean. He must supervise the work of skin-divers who risk their lives at the bottom of the sea. He must work in the deserts of Mongolia, in Russia, and in China. He must care more for his search than for his comfort, and for his reward he must feel that adding even one small fragment to the world's knowledge of its past is an achievement that makes all his efforts worthwhile.

No book could tell of all the enterprises, successful and unsuccessful, which archaeologists have undertaken in the last hundred years, and this one does not. It tells of the work of a few men, though there are hundreds of others whose stories might be told. But here are some accounts of the wonder of the early discoverers and of the way in which modern science has helped the later ones. The story begins with the discovery of some statues that a bride once wanted to put into her garden.

2.

Some Statues for a Bride's Garden

The ancient Roman town of Herculaneum was built on the slope of a hillside that overlooks the Bay of Naples, but its neighboring town of Pompeii was only about a mile from the foot of Mount Vesuvius. The two towns flourished in the first century of the Christian era. Many retired Roman citizens built villas overlooking the sea at Herculaneum, and their presence gave the town a quiet, rich, luxurious atmosphere. But Pompeii was filled with bustle and activity: many came to see the gladiatorial combats in the amphitheater there.

The citizens of these old towns paid little heed to the volcano that towered over them. It had been quiet for as long as they could remember, and they were concerned with

their own affairs. In 63 A.D., it is true, there had been a tidal
wave that sank many boats of the fishing fleet and destroyed
houses along the shore of the Bay. This had been accompanied by an earthquake — the roofs of houses, temples, and
other buildings had fallen in, and in one place there was a
crack in the earth so big that a flock of six hundred sheep
disappeared into it. Some people thought the volcano was
connected with these happenings, but most of them ignored
the warning, and went to work to build new roofs and to
restore what had been harmed.

Then, early on the morning of August 24 in the year 79
A.D., the catastrophe occurred. The people of both towns
heard a tremendous explosion and looked up to see the top of
Mount Vesuvius split in two. Bright tongues of flame were
shooting up into the morning sky, and billowing clouds of
smoke darkened the sun. As they watched, they saw the
brightness of the summer morning turn into twilight.

Herculaneum was overwhelmed by the catastrophe first.
There it began to rain heavily, soaking the cloaks of those
who ran down the streets. The rushing water soon became
mud, and the mud was followed by streams of thick molten
rock, or lava, that grew deeper and deeper until it was impossible for anyone to move from one place to another. Soon
the flowing lava rose to the tops of the doors and windows
and then mounted to the roof tops, until it covered the entire
city and everything in it. It solidified afterward into a sheet
of rock which averaged about sixty feet in thickness. But all
this took a number of hours: the people had time to collect

their valuables and to hitch up horses and mules to flee. Relatively few citizens of Herculaneum lost their lives.

In Pompeii the story was different. That town, though it was near the foot of the volcano, was not in the course of the flowing lava. The Pompeiians saw the volcano belch out its flames and smoke, and they saw it toss its rocks and cinders into the sky, but they thought they would be safe. They did not know that the wind would change and set toward their city. With that wind a fine, white dust from the volcano came blowing down upon them. They brushed it from their shoulders and held their cloaks up to their faces in order to breathe. Then cinders and small stones called *lapilli* came rattling down, and when the stones grew bigger and became dangerous, people took refuge indoors.

The showers of cinders and stones continued to fall on Pompeii for hours, and soon they lay so heavy on the house tops that the roofs collapsed, crushing the people beneath them. All this time sulfur fumes blew down on the city so that those who were not crushed were stifled.

Eventually the hot ashes, which had piled high on the ruined houses and streets, cooled and hardened, forming a plaster mold around the objects beneath them. It encased the bodies of the fleeing citizens. Men, women, children, dogs — all were caught and held at whatever they were doing, their bodies imprisoned in the solidified ashes for centuries to come.

The eruption lasted all day and all night. In twenty-eight hours it was over, and the sun came out again. But Herculaneum and Pompeii were gone. The cities that shortly before had been filled with vigorous life were no more to be seen. They had completely disappeared.

Some of the refugees from Herculaneum came back to the site of their city when the lava had cooled and tried to dig down through it to recover their possessions. But few returned to the place where Pompeii had been: nearly all of her citizens were dead.

As the years passed no one dared to rebuild the unfortunate cities. Their sites were deserted, and they were forgotten for more than sixteen hundred years.

In the eighteenth century an architect, Prince d'Elbeuf, was ordered by the Bourbon King Charles of Naples to erect a group of new buildings; the Bourbons had recently taken over the rule of Italy, calling their domain the Kingdom of the Two Sicilies.

Upon receiving his commission Prince d'Elbeuf began at once to search the Italian peninsula for fragments of marble which he could crush to make lime for his buildings. He had not searched far when one day some peasants told him they had found pieces of marble in some pits near the Bay of Naples, and d'Elbeuf went to investigate.

The site to which the peasants took him was near the foot of Mount Vesuvius. The ancient cities of Pompeii and Herculaneum had once stood here, and when d'Elbeuf reached the place to which the peasants directed him, he found that already they had unearthed a number of marble statues. Some of these were broken, but some were still intact, and he thought them quite beautiful. They seemed too fine indeed to be destroyed, and he had them taken to show his monarch, King Charles.

Now it happened that King Charles had married recently and he was building a new palace for his bride. The palace was to be surrounded by elaborate gardens. What could be more suitable, the monarch thought, than to adorn these gardens with the marble statues which Prince d'Elbeuf had found?

The bride, whose name was Maria Amalia Christine, was enchanted with the ancient statuary. Could her husband not get more of it? she asked. Eager to please his bride, the King now organized an expedition to search for ancient statues near the place where the first ones had been found. The leader of this expedition was a Spaniard, the commanding officer of the Royal Engineers, Cavaliere Rocco Gioacchino de Alcubierre. He took about sixty men with him, and with picks and shovels they set out to look for ancient statuary.

Alcubierre planned to go down a well shaft which d'Elbeuf had found and to cut tunnels leading out from it. They had not dug long when the picks the men wielded were ringing against metal, and the diggers were bringing to the surface not marble statuary but the fragments of three bronze equestrian statues of heroic size. After that they brought up the marble figures of several Romans in their togas, some painted columns, and a big bronze horse.

When news of these finds was brought to the King and his bride, they went themselves to inspect the excavations. And when they reached the site, the King decided to allow himself to be lowered into the shaft by a rope, while his bride peered down at him over the edge of the hole.

Soon after, at the bottom of the hole, the diggers made another discovery. By the light of a lantern, they saw a flight of stairs.

That flight of stairs led straight to the center of what turned out to be a stage. The roof of the theater had fallen in, the back wall had collapsed with the weight of the lava rolling against it, and the floor was littered with broken statuary. Not until several weeks later, however, that is on December 11, 1738, was an inscription found which gave the name of the city in which this theater had stood. *"Theatrum Herculanensi,"* the inscription read. They had found the city of Herculaneum. A little more digging would have uncovered the houses and the streets that had lain undisturbed for more than seventeen centuries.

But Cavaliere Alcubierre must have lacked imagination, or curiosity, or whatever other quality it is that makes men dig with passionate persistence. He decided that he would abandon the shaft and have it sealed up. So once more Herculaneum, that rich, luxurious town, was temporarily abandoned.

Some years later Alcubierre started his digging again, and this time he began to penetrate the ashes that covered the nearby town of Pompeii. It was much easier to dig down through the ashes than it had been to pierce the hardened lava at Herculaneum. On April 6, 1748, Alcubierre and his men uncovered a wall painting at Pompeii, its colors still brilliant and perfectly preserved. Then, about two weeks later, they found the skeleton of a man encrusted in the ashes. The man was stretched out full length, and gold and silver coins had rolled away from his clutching hands. When the city was overwhelmed, that summer morning in 79 A.D., he apparently had tried to escape with his treasure, but there was not time, and he had died like the other citizens of that doomed town.

Bony skeletons and painted walls were not what King Charles and his bride and their excavator Alcubierre were looking for, however. So they searched further and found more bronze and marble statuary, which the King ordered brought to his palace.

Rumors of these discoveries soon spread, and students began to inquire about them. Those who had read history knew of the Roman towns that had disappeared when Vesuvius erupted so long ago, and they wanted to see the objects that Alcubierre had unearthed. King Charles, however, was not ready to share his finds with the rest of the world. He kept the treasures he had brought from Pompeii and Herculaneum behind locked doors and inside carefully guarded walls. In learned circles the discoveries at Pompeii and Herculaneum were discussed and speculated upon, but no one outside the royal court was permitted to set eyes on them.

Soon after the sculptures from Pompeii and Herculaneum had been set up in the garden of the King of Naples, and armed guards had been employed to see that no one entered either the garden or the area where the statues had been found, Johann Joachim Winckelmann, a German student of art, asked permission to visit the excavations. Like all other petitions of this kind, his was denied.

But Winckelmann was not easily discouraged. He was determined that somehow he would see and study the treasures that were guarded so carefully.

This Winckelmann was the son of a shoemaker, and though he was poor, he had managed to support himself by teaching school. In those lean years of his teaching he studied Greek and Roman history at night and read eagerly, so the people of antiquity were as real to him as his own people. By the time he was thirty-seven he had decided that he must visit the places where the ancient peoples had lived.

He began by going to Rome. There the thin, passionate scholar with his quick movements and burning eyes joined the Roman Catholic Church and became librarian to a cardinal who had a great collection of ancient manuscripts.

Being librarian gave Winckelmann time to study. Soon he became an authority on ancient art, comparing various pieces which had been found in different parts of Europe. In 1764 he was appointed chief supervisor of all antiquities in and about Rome. It was in that capacity that he tried in vain to get permission to visit Pompeii and Herculaneum.

He finally succeeded, not by virtue of his position but because of his persistent nature. He bribed a workman who let him slip through the fence that surrounded the Pompeiian excavations. He did the same thing at Herculaneum.

What he saw behind those fences stirred him beyond measure. He went again and again and examined each fragment of marble, each wall painting and stone column. It was absurd to keep all these findings secret, he said. The scholars of the world ought to know what rare treasures of the ancient past had been uncovered here. He wrote an open letter in which he described what he had seen, and he published it so that all might read. This open letter was followed some time later by his great book, the *History of the Art of Antiquity*.

This was an epoch-making book, for in it Winckelmann had hit upon a new idea. He announced that the sculpture, buildings, and furniture preserved from the ancient past should be studied, not only for their intrinsic beauty, but also because these works revealed the ways and customs of the men who had made them. If enough ancient objects could be recovered, a scholar might find out not only what clothing these ancient people wore, with what jewelry they adorned themselves, what weapons they used, but also what kind of houses they lived in, how they amused themselves, what gods they worshiped. Add all this information to the knowledge already available through books, and the people who had been dust for centuries would come alive again.

It is true that the people of the Renaissance had admired the ancient Roman structures and had loved the grace, delicacy, and strength of the marble statues they found. Nevertheless, they had shown very little curiosity about their makers. Preoccupied, perhaps, with their own affairs, they had not troubled to inquire much about them. Only now, after Winckelmann had managed to slip through the gates of Pompeii and Herculaneum, only after he had had the courage to publish his open letter and his great book, did scholars realize that here was a key that would open the doors to the past, and here were clues that might lead them back to a life that was gone. Here indeed was a weapon that could be wielded against the universal enemy, time.

The effort to reconstruct the past through studying the objects that former generations have left behind them is archaeology; and Johann Joachim Winckelmann may fairly be named the first true archaeologist.

The rewards which Winckelmann reaped for all his effort were ironically the cause of his untimely death. In 1768 he went back to his native Germany; there he was heaped with honors by admiring scholars. On the journey back to Rome, he stopped in Austria, where the Empress Maria Theresa presented him with a gold medal. After leaving Austria, while staying overnight at an inn in Trieste, he made the acquaintance of a stranger named Arcangeli, to whom he showed the gold medal. Early the next morning Arcangeli entered his room and murdered him, then escaped, taking the medal with him.

But the fascination Winckelmann felt for the relics of Pompeii and Herculaneum — the fascination of archaeology — communicated itself to many others after his death. As time passed, more and more archaeological expeditions went to Pompeii and Herculaneum. By tireless work those old cities were completely uncovered, so that today they stand almost as they did that summer morning in 79 A.D. when the roaring volcano snuffed the life out of them.

3.

Napoleon Sparks the Interest in Egypt

Everywhere at the end of the eighteenth century people were talking of the great discoveries of Pompeii and Herculaneum. They were speculating about the men who had peopled the earth centuries ago, and wondering what ancient treasures they themselves might be lucky enough to find. Even Napoleon Bonaparte, occupied as he was with his plans for world conquest, felt a curiosity about the past.

Napoleon set off on his Egyptian campaign in 1798, bound to assert French supremacy in the Mediterranean. The French people saw his huge fleet and his forty thousand picked soldiers, and they swore that never had such a splendid force been assembled anywhere.

But Napoleon had more in mind than the supremacy of France in the Eastern Mediterranean. He had heard of the ruins of vast temples that towered above the encroaching sands of Egypt and of imposing obelisks and pyramids; he was determined that he would claim all these for France. Hence, he took with him not only his best troops, but also a band of "savants," or scholars, to study the ancient relics. There were about 120 of these learned gentlemen, and they were the most erudite scholars in France at the time. They armed themselves before they sailed with an extensive library of the writings of ancient authors.

With these savants and his soldiers, Napoleon landed in Alexandria, but he did not linger there. He marched on across the desert to Cairo. On that march his army suffered greatly, for they had to contend with heat, thirst, and hunger. The savants suffered too and complained especially that they had to drink slimy cistern water. Some men died on the march, and a few committed suicide.

But the hardier men came at last to Cairo, and then to the pyramids at Giza. Napoleon stopped at the base of the tallest of them to address his army.

"Soldiers," he said, "from the summit of these pyramids forty centuries are looking down at you."

The French troops had not been long in Egypt when Napoleon met with disaster. Lord Nelson and the British fleet sailed down the Mediterranean and won a resounding victory at the Battle of the Nile. The vanquished French general, not daunted, returned to Paris to make other plans, but his

army still held the Valley of the Nile. The savants with their library stayed on, too, busy with their studies.

The towering stone columns, the pyramids in their precise beauty, the graceful shafts of the obelisks — all these were an enigma to the awed scholars who looked up at them. What were the people like who made these objects? When had they been built? Whence had the stones been brought for those mammoth structures? There were no quarries nearby in the Valley of the Nile. And the most learned of the scholars could not read the strange inscriptions that were cut so clearly in the enduring stone, for the writing was not like any they had ever seen before. Hours of study and patient searching through their books did not help them.

So the scholars contented themselves with sketching the great monuments and writing long descriptive papers. Every five days they met and read the papers, which were later published in many volumes under the title *Description de l'Égypte*, the first great work on Egyptology.

Despite their learned papers, however, the scholars were still mystified by the inscriptions that they found engraved on walls and pillars. They continued unceasingly their efforts to decipher them but met with no success. Then, quite unexpectedly, the key to the problem was found.

In 1799 a French officer named Boussard, directing some excavations for a fort near the Rosetta Mouth of the Nile, came upon a slab of stone which was covered with a long inscription. Here is another inscription that no one can read, he must have thought. But he instructed his men to take up the stone carefully and carry it back to the place where the savants were working.

The Rosetta Stone, as it was later to be called, is a smooth slab of black basalt. When the scholars examined it they found that the writing on it was of three different kinds. The inscriptions on the upper part of the slab consisted of the same type of "hieroglyphs," or small pictures, that was carved on the walls of Egypt. But below there were lines written in a cursive hand, and the third script, at the bottom of the stone, was in Greek which the scholars could read. The Greek script was the key with which they hoped to solve the puzzle. Surely, they reasoned, the message on this stone might very well be a single one, written in three different ways.

They worked eagerly, for they felt certain that here they would find a way to read the Egyptian inscriptions. But they were not given the satisfaction of finishing their task, for in 1801 the French were defeated by the English again and forced to leave the Valley of the Nile. The Rosetta Stone was taken to England and put in the British Museum. There the scientist and scholar Thomas Young studied the writing and made some headway toward deciphering it. Later the young Frenchman Jean François Champollion completed the work that the others had begun.

The inscriptions in their three different kinds of writing did, indeed, have the same meaning. The one in hieroglyphics was the writing commonly employed by the priests and was used therefore on temple walls and tombs. The second was in demotic script, so called because the word *demos* means people; this was the writing generally used in business. The third was in Greek, probably because so many Greeks had settled near the mouth of the Nile. The meaning of the three was found to be identical. It was a decree from the priests of Memphis declaring that Ptolemy V was the rightful ruler of Egypt.

After Champollion's decipherment of the Rosetta Stone, Egyptian inscriptions were no longer secret. The walls of tombs and temples and the slender shafts of obelisks were now open books. Here were accounts of the reigns of kings, of their relations with their neighbors, their business dealings, their achievements in battle. Now it was possible to unfold the whole long story of Egypt's past, to make lists of her rulers, to assign dates to them.

All that had seemed strange, confused, and distant was now immediate and real. The public clamored to see the huge stone images of the Pharaohs, to examine the ancient hieroglyphics. And museum directors enlarged their buildings to accommodate the towering relics brought from Egypt across the Mediterranean.

Collecting these gigantic objects for display at museums required much energy and an adventurous spirit. It was necessary for the collector to make business deals with the local sheiks, and this was by no means easy. Moreover, at that time, the Nile Valley was infested with lawless brigands and robber gangs who often set upon travelers, threatening their lives. Added to these difficulties there were the dirty native inns, the discomforts of travel, the heat, the dust, the thirst.

Still, a good many men went out in search of Egyptian relics for the museums; the prices they could get were generally high. One of the most adventurous of these was an Italian named Giovanni Belzoni, a former weight-lifter in a circus, who attacked the ancient tombs and temples with battering rams to tear out fragments that he could sell to museums in various parts of Europe. Another was French — Auguste Mariette, who nearly lost his life when he was set on by a band of robbers. He managed to collect 143 sphinxes, many of which he succeeded in bringing back to Europe. Others made indiscriminate collections of everything they could find, saddling the museums with all sorts of objects.

While the roving collectors were busy loading the Mediterranean ships with heavy stone objects bound for Europe, and the public was crowding the museum halls to marvel at the colossal relics, Flinders Petrie, a young English archaeologist working in Egypt, observed what was going on with great distaste. Afflicted with asthma and delicate from his birth, he had, nevertheless, a mind that was clear and determined. And he had respect for the ancient relics that the dry air of Egypt had preserved through the centuries. He admired their size and grandeur, but these were not the qualities that interested him most. He believed that small, unimpressive objects might indeed be fully as useful in finding out the ways of past generations as were the grand and magnificent ones. He looked on every broken bit of pottery, every rusty iron tool, with the same eager interest. And he examined not only the objects themselves but also the place where they lay, and the position of each in relation to other objects. He sketched, making accurate measurements, and kept a record of every object he found. Later he wrote careful descriptions so that other scholars might be informed of what he had done. Such methodical and painstaking work would have astonished the ruthless Belzoni.

Petrie worked at a number of different places in the Valley of the Nile. He worked at the great temple at Tanis, and also at Fayum, and he discovered and explored the long lost Greek city of Naucratis near the Delta of the Nile. But his most interesting work was done in 1880 at the Great Pyramid at Giza.

The pyramids had been built by the early kings of Egypt as burial places for their own bodies after death. Many other men besides Napoleon had looked up at them with awe and had wondered at the beauty of the stonecutters' work, for the great blocks of limestone were fitted together so precisely that no mortar was needed to hold them in place. The Great Pyramid at Giza had been rifled many times; the valuable objects buried with the Pharaohs had long since disappeared, but Petrie was not especially interested in things that had intrinsic value. He wanted to find out about the engineering feats of that ancient people. How had they made those great structures, the biggest of which covered nearly 14 acres and towered up nearly 500 feet? He wanted to know to what uses the various parts of the building had been put, and he wanted to find out all he could about the people who made it.

Petrie worked alone. He made his headquarters in a small

tomb near the pyramids, where he established himself in a little chamber that he thought had been used to store offerings for the dead. There, because the heat in the Nile Valley is intense, he slept through most of the daylight hours and cooked his meals on a kerosene stove. When night came he stripped to the waist, the better to bear the heat while working, took his lantern and his notebook, and crossed the hot sands to the entrance of the Great Pyramid, which was half-buried in sand.

He worked all night inside the Pyramid. The air was close and hot, and the dust nearly strangled him. But night after night he kept on with his work, examining every corner, every passageway, and the chamber whence the Pharaoh's mummified body had long since been stolen away. Coughing and exhausted, he emerged in the morning to take refuge in the chamber which was his temporary home.

Petrie's work gave a new impetus to the study of Egypt's past. Soon other scholars came to work in the Valley of the Nile, and gradually Egypt's long history unfolded before their eyes. They were able to make a list of all the Pharaohs from the first one to the last. They studied their temples and their tombs, and soon knew of all their exploits and their glorious conquests. In paintings on the walls of tombs they were able to follow the Pharaohs as they hunted game in Nubia and reedbirds in the marshes along the Nile; they saw them feasting at rich banquets or listening to the music of their court musicians. They saw not only the Pharaohs and their queens, but humble people as well — those who waited on the monarchs and made their life possible. The farmer and the beekeeper were here, and so were the workers in the vineyards and the threshers of the grain. Here, too, were the scribes with their papyrus rolls, the textile workers weaving fine linens, the jewelers, the potters, and many others.

After Petrie had published his reports, there was another great surge of interest in Egypt, this time not among the museum public but among the archaeologists. Soon archaeologists from many countries were converging in Egypt. The dryness of that country's climate, her long history, and the wealth of her Pharaohs — all combined to give rich promise to any undertaking here. The methods for investigation and reporting which Flinders Petrie had developed, as well as new scientific techniques of preserving whatever they might find, made them confident that their work would be rewarded.

By the beginning of the twentieth century Egypt's history was almost as well known as that of the United States. But as one expedition after another published its findings, it was disappointing to discover that very little that was new appeared. Tomb-robbers had sacked the tombs and temples so thoroughly that whenever archaeologists excavated a tomb they found it had been rifled.

It was just at this point that the Englishman Howard Carter decided to make one more search in the tombs of the Valley of the Kings near Thebes; the Earl of Carnarvon agreed to finance Carter's expedition.

Carter worked five years and in November 1922 he was just about to abandon his efforts when he thought he would make

one more try. He cleared away what he thought might have
been some workmen's huts and found a flight of steps cut in
the stone beneath them. After working for several days,
Carter discovered what was undoubtedly the entrance to a
tomb. He sent a telegram to Lord Carnarvon, who joined him
two weeks later. Workmen cleared rubble from the passageway to the tomb and penetrated the door. Carter entered and
came to a second door. He made a hole in it and, with Carnarvon, gazed at marvelous things. When the door was later
opened, the two men saw two huge statues of black basalt.
Some golden objects were scattered on the floor. The robbers
evidently had been here before him; it looked as if they had
been frightened off. Behind the statues a third door was
securely fastened. Had the robbers opened this and fastened
it again?

Before opening the third door, Carter and his men spent
weeks carefully removing objects from the antechamber and
from a smaller room which they had discovered. It was not
until February 1923 that they found the burial chamber of
Tutankhamen, the young son-in-law of the Pharaoh Ikhnaton.
Inside this chamber, Carter came to a golden shrine — and a
second shrine within it; nearby, he also found a separate
room filled with treasures. Everywhere the articles that
might be useful to Tutankhamen in his future life were
heaped: chairs and couches, chariots, little shrines and uten-
sils, articles of clothing and jewelry. Every object shone
with a blaze of color that had not dimmed with the passing
of years. Carter admired one lovely object after another.

Examining these things, marveling at the work of the craftsmen who had made them, Howard Carter and his staff recorded each article and photographed it. (Those pictures, which he sent back to England, were a rich display for the newspapers.) He treated each object with preservatives before it was taken carefully from the tomb where it had lain so many centuries. Perhaps the archaeologists had known all there was to know of Egypt and her past, but surely they had not ever before witnessed the delicacy and beauty of her craftsmanship, the grace of design in the tracery on golden goblet or enameled cup, the gossamer thinness of the fine linens, the richness of the golden jewelry.

This work took several years (Carnarvon had died in 1923), and it was not until 1926 that Carter re-entered the golden shrines and found the body of the Pharaoh, carefully wrapped and beautifully encased, lying as it had lain for three thousand years, since the day his subjects placed it there. This was indeed an exciting moment in archaeology.

Standing in the dark tomb after the last of Tutankhamen's treasures had been recorded, photographed, carefully packed, and crated to be sent to the museum at Cairo, Howard Carter must have felt that the disk of Pharaoh's sun god itself had shone down on him. For he was the first who had laid eyes on all these things for more than three thousand years.

Perhaps he felt a debt of gratitude, too, to Flinders Petrie, who had taught him that the wealth of ancient Egypt should not be sought with a battering ram, but should be carefully unearthed, studied, and preserved.

4.

The Mounds of Mesopotamia

While museum directors in Europe were filling their galleries with Egyptian objects, a river valley whose culture was as old as Egypt's lay unexplored and little heard of. This was Mesopotamia, the land between the Tigris and Euphrates rivers. The Bible said that the Euphrates was the "River of Paradise," but a French writer in the nineteenth century described the valley as "the beige country." The words seem apt, for in that valley the soil, the mud houses, and the reeds with which they were roofed were the same shade of brown.

Yet for all the drabness of the land now called Iraq, travelers who visited the valley a hundred years ago said there was a sheen of greenness over it in the spring. They said hundreds of "tells," or low mounds, threw their dark shadows across the plain, covered with waving grass and wild flowers. There were the bleating of sheep and the lowing of cattle as the flocks and herds returned from their pastures to wander among the Arab tents. Girls moved among them, too, carrying pitchers on their heads or loads of grass they had cut in the pastures. Sometimes a group of horsemen galloped by, while at night the whole plain glittered with innumerable fires.

A hundred years ago the people who lived in the river valley thought the mounds which were everywhere around them must certainly have been man-made, but they knew very little else about them. We know now that they were built up slowly by successive accumulations of the remains of early dwellings. Time and again villages and small towns on these sites were destroyed by war, earthquake, or fire and then were rebuilt. When the inhabitants reconstructed their houses, they did not trouble to clear away the debris of their former dwellings but reduced the rubble to a new building level. On this they reared their dwelling houses again, their temples and their palaces. Anyone who troubled to slice down through one of these mounds, therefore, would find a series of layers with bricks, tools, weapons, and ornaments scattered through them. Until a little more than a century ago, however, no one troubled to investigate the mounds. For many years the country had been ruled by the Turks and, although modern Turkey is much interested in archaeology, a hundred years ago they knew nothing of it.

Still, European travelers to the valley had wondered about the mounds for generations. Why were the mounds there and what did they hide? One of the largest was on the bank of the Tigris River where the present oil center of Mosul is situated. Another was south of Baghdad on the left bank of the Euphrates. Arabs and Jews agreed that these were the sites of ancient Nineveh and Babylon, the wicked cities that the Lord was said to have destroyed. Those who came to the valley wondered about Babylon and Nineveh while they picked up bits of broken pottery and fragments of brick covered with illegible inscriptions. In the middle of the nineteenth century the mounds gave up the secrets buried in them for five thousand years, and the kings of the valley, with their splendor, their triumphs, and their conquests, were brought back to life.

The great discoveries in that ancient river valley started in a mild enough way. If a date is wanted, put down 1808 when Claudius James Rich and his wife Mary traveled from England to Baghdad. Claudius Rich was twenty-one then, and his wife was younger. He had been appointed to the post of Resident in Baghdad by the East India Company. The new appointee had an extraordinary gift for languages: he knew Persian, Arabic, Hebrew, and Syriac, as well as a little Chinese. He also had a great charm of manner and tact in getting along with people, so the East India Company thought their new man a valuable one.

Claudius Rich and his wife made their entry into Baghdad with some ostentation, wanting to impress the Turks with whom they were to live. Claudius rode at the head of his mounted sepoy guard, and behind him Mary was carried in a palanquin, accompanied by a bodyguard of Armenian servants.

They lived in a large Turkish house which had three courts, one of them originally intended for a harem. In summer the heat mounted at noon to 122 degrees, so they did not go outdoors during the day except in the very early morning. After dark they dined on the terrace, and generally they slept there too, for no one in Baghdad wanted to sleep in a house on those hot nights.

In winter, however, once the first rains had laid the dust and the mud had dried, riding was possible. Then Claudius mounted his horse, but Mary preferred to ride a donkey. She dressed like a native woman for these rides; a black veil covered her face, and she was enveloped in a blue mantle which allowed only her feet, clad in yellow boots, to be seen.

Life at the residency in Baghdad was dull for the young couple in spite of the excitement of occasional quarrels with the Pasha. Travelers from Europe seldom came there, and the Riches amused themselves with excursions into the country, often visiting the mounds, which held great fascination for them. Sometimes they picked up curious odds and ends which they carried back to the residency.

In time Claudius Rich went farther in exploring the valley. He visited the site of the ruined city of Babylon in 1811 and collected some specimens of clay tablets that bore what were apparently undecipherable inscriptions. At least it seemed to Rich that the "cuneiform" or wedge-shaped characters on the tablets were a kind of writing, but they might be merely parts of an intricate design — he could not be sure.

What had Babylon been like? he wondered. He drew a plan of the site of the ancient city, making a careful survey of the place. The more he studied the terrain, the more excited he became, and his excitement was reflected in his *Memoir of the Ruins of Babylon* which he sent to London to be published. Similar manuscripts followed the first one.

Rich did not attempt any excavation of the mound where Babylon once stood, but he worked the surface of the earth with great care and thoroughness — the first lone worker in a task that later was to attract hundreds of talented archaeologists.

The Near East then was an unhealthful place, and Claudius Rich, for all his enthusiasm and will to live, could not escape an epidemic of cholera that raged in the valley. He died of the disease in 1821.

Mary, returning to London after his death, sold the objects they had collected to the British Museum. The museum paid 7000 pounds sterling for what was recognized as "an extensive and valuable collection of antiquities."

The collection consisted of "cylinders, amulets, idols and intaglios of the most curious kind." Many of those pieces bore inscriptions. The museum directors listed "thirty-two clay tablets and fragments inscribed in cuneiform; thirteen bricks stamped with inscriptions in Babylonian characters; one black stone memorial tablet inscribed in cuneiform; one large inscribed boundary stone."

No one at the British Museum, or anywhere else for that matter, could read the inscriptions these objects bore. The most learned scholars could not guess the meaning of the wedge-shaped characters.

5.

Henry Rawlinson and the Wild Kurdish Boy

It is interesting to wonder how long those mysterious objects that Mary Rich sold the British Museum would have lain in their glass cases, meaningless, had not the German schoolmaster George Friedrich Grotefend and the English soldier Henry Rawlinson found ways of deciphering cuneiform writings.

Grotefend, to be sure, received little credit for what he did while he was living. He had been fascinated by trying to read Persian cuneiform. Travelers had brought back to Europe copies of inscriptions engraved on the walls of Persian palaces, and scholars had recognized that some of them were written in three different kinds of cuneiform and seemed to be trilingual; that is, each script might correspond to a different language. Two of the Persian scripts were different from the cuneiform found on Babylonian objects, but the third seemed to be the same.

Grotefend worked on one of the languages which he believed was alphabetical rather than syllabic. He studied the form of later Persian inscriptions and concluded from these models that a recurring set of cuneiform characters stood for the word *King* and another for the phrase *son of*. Then, after consulting the Greek historian Herodotus on Persian history, ingeniously and patiently he applied what he had discovered: he could read the words, "Darius, the King, the King of kings, son of Hystaspes," and "Xerxes, the King, the King of kings, son of Darius, the King."

But German philologists would give Grotefend no credit. For ninety years his work was unrecognized while the objects Claudius Rich had found lay undeciphered in the British Museum.

Meantime in 1835 Henry Creswicke Rawlinson was stationed at Kermanshah as military adviser to the brother of the Shah of Persia, and Kermanshah is only twenty-two miles from the little village of Behistun. Near there a great inscription is carved on the face of a rocky cliff overhanging the road where for generations caravans have passed on their way from Babylon to the Persian Plateau. Henry Rawlinson became much interested in that rock and its inscription; he rode over to look at it often.

The Behistun Rock inscription covers an area which is 25 feet high and 50 feet wide at a height of 350 feet up the

precipitous mountain side. The living stone on which the inscription was carved had been carefully smoothed and uneven places in it had been replaced with more suitable material. After the carving was completed, the whole surface was covered with a thick coat of varnish whose surface was tougher than the stone itself. In places where the varnish had been loosened by moisture great flakes of it had fallen on the ledge below, and some of these bore a clear impression of the lettering they had covered.

Because of its inaccessible location, earlier travelers had been content to view the inscription through a telescope. But Rawlinson was not satisfied to see it from a distance: he wanted to get close to it, to make "squeezes," or copies, by pressing wet clay against the stone and letting it dry there before it was removed. To make squeezes of such a tremendous inscription would be extraordinarily difficult, but Rawlinson was filled with youthful enterprise: he wanted to try it.

For several years Rawlinson spent a great deal of time at the rock: its inaccessibility was a fascinating challenge. He was an athlete and an experienced climber, and he reached the lower part without much difficulty. But when he got to the upper part, he had to bring ropes and ladders. Finally there were sections that even ropes and ladders would not reach. It looked as if the last parts of the inscription would never be read.

"At length, however," he wrote later, "a wild Kurdish boy who had come from a distance volunteered to make the attempt." The boy pushed himself up through a cleft in the rock, drove a stake to which he could attach a rope, swung himself out over the face of the rock, drove another stake, and attached the rope again. In this way he succeeded in making a kind of swinging seat. Henry Rawlinson, clinging to a ledge below, shouted up directions about how the squeezes should be made.

So, piece by piece, Rawlinson and the Kurdish boy made copies of the huge inscription which Darius the Great, "King of kings, King of Persia" had caused to be carved on the rock, and these were brought down from the cliff and taken to a place where Rawlinson could study them.

After painstaking work Rawlinson discovered that the great inscription was an announcement of how King Darius of Persia had triumphed over his enemies. The face of the rock was divided into four sections. The section at the top was sculptured in bas-relief. It showed King Darius with his foot resting on the dead body of one of his enemies while other conquered kings walked before him, roped together neck to neck. The symbol of Ahura-Mazda, Persian god of light, shines down on the mighty monarch.

This picture was well calculated to impress the caravans that passed along the road below, even if they did not stop to read the inscriptions. But for those who did, the announcement was more specific. Here in grand superlatives was the statement of the Persian monarch's might and power. Three separate languages were used to make the great announcement, for Darius ruled over many peoples and wanted no misunderstanding.

The same message was written on three separate panels of the rock, each inscribed with a different kind of cuneiform. The first was in the Persian cuneiform which Grotefend had deciphered. The second was in another type of cuneiform which was later found to be that used by the Babylonians. And the third was in the cuneiform used by the people of Elam and was therefore called Elamite. These facts were deduced by Rawlinson only after ten years of study.

Rawlinson published the results of his work in 1850, and his report caused great excitement in Europe. Reading the ancient Persian script as Grotefend had done was interesting but not of the greatest importance: not many of the ancient Persian inscriptions had been preserved. But the translation of the languages of the Mesopotamian valley, and especially of the Babylonian cuneiform was another matter.

For thousands of years no one had been able to read the cuneiform of Babylonia or to study the records hidden in the mounds of the Mesopotamian valley. Twenty-five hundred years of history which had been forgotten could be recovered by patient scholarship. Now a large group of scholars who called themselves "Assyriologists" started to decipher the inscriptions on objects being brought from Mesopotamia to Europe in greater and greater numbers.

6.

The Winged Bulls of Assyria

After the memoirs of Claudius Rich were published post-humously and Rawlinson had deciphered the ancient Persian inscription on the Behistun Rock, there was much talk of Assyria in Europe and much speculation about the people who had lived in the valley between the Tigris and the Euphrates so many thousands of years ago. There was talk about the Babylonians too, but no one knew that a still earlier people, the Sumerians, had once flourished in the valley. Their civilization had disappeared completely and was not rediscovered until after the First World War when

Charles Leonard Woolley began to investigate the site where they had lived.

In the mid-eighteenth century, however, the Assyrians caught the popular imagination. No one knew much about them to be sure except that there were references in the Old Testament to their fierce warriors and their ruthless kings; and they were said to have been a scourge to the people in the valley.

The fact that so very little was known about the Assyrians explains why the work of Paul Émile Botta created such a stir. In 1842 he was appointed French consul at Mosul, but he was more interested in archaeology than in diplomacy. Perhaps he accepted the appointment because he knew that his duties would not be very arduous. The new French consul had not been in residence long when he started excavations on a great mound on the border of the Tigris River not far from Mosul. He worked patiently for nearly a year, with no success at all. Discouraged, he was about to give up his digging, when one of his workmen told him of another mound not far away at Khorsabad. The Arab said that he himself had seen inscribed stones on the ground there. Doubting, but still interested, Botta decided to try digging at Khorsabad.

Almost as soon as his men's spades began to turn the earth of the grassy mound, Botta was successful. For here he found what he thought was Nineveh but later proved to be the ruins of the palace of the great King Sargon who ruled Assyria from 722 to 705 B.C. The palace was so big that it covered 25 acres, and it was built on a brick terrace 45 feet high.

There were hundreds of rooms and corridors lined with miles of alabaster friezes in bas-relief. Botta obtained the services of an artist named Flandin to make drawings of the friezes.

Then Botta sent a message back to Paris announcing, "Nineveh has been found!" and many French people were wildly excited. The French government appropriated a handsome sum of money to have his report published in five beautiful volumes, and these were illustrated with steel engravings of Flandin's sketches. The fact that Botta was mistaken in thinking he had found Nineveh made his discoveries no less beautiful or interesting.

Meantime the memoirs of Claudius Rich had stirred the interest of another young man. Austen Henry Layard was a clerk in a London solicitor's office, but he had been accustomed to spending his spare time studying the Persian language and dreaming of the Arabian East. When he was offered a position in Ceylon, he decided that he would go there overland and on foot. The journey would take him near the places which Rich had described: he would be near the ground on which the Assyrians had once walked. He had only 200 pounds sterling to spend on the trip. It was not much, but he would make it do.

For two years Layard wandered through the wild and remote corners of Persia and Arabia. Several times he was set upon by Arabian tribesmen and robbed of his clothes and money. And then, penniless and half-naked, he was befriended by a European diplomat or a local potentate. Once he was reported wearing a Persian costume, the crown of his head shaved "leaving a ringlet on either side" and his "hair and beard dyed . . . with henna. . . ." Subsequently he was seen walking along the dusty roads wearing an Arabian "aba" or a Turkish "tarboosh."

The traveler finally sailed down the Tigris on a creaking raft, or *kelek*, supported on inflated skins, and when he saw the great mound near the river's bank at Nimrud, he gave up all ideas of going to Ceylon.

It was near sunset when Layard first saw Nimrud; the mound was casting a long shadow across the plain. From that moment he could think of nothing save what he might be able to find inside that heap of earth. He wrote later of the "stern, shapeless mound rising like a hill from the scorching plain, the fragments of pottery and the stupendous mass of brick work occasionally laid bare by the winter rain." By 1846 he had collected sufficient money to start full-scale excavations. He enlisted the help of Hormuzd Rassam, a Coptic Christian who would act as overseer and general aid, and having got permission to dig from the government at Baghdad, the two men arrived at Nimrud one evening just before dark.

Layard wrote later that he could not sleep that night. "Visions of palaces underground, of gigantic monsters, of sculptured figures and endless inscriptions floated before me. After forming plan after plan for removing the earth and extricating these treasures, I fancied myself wandering in a maze of chambers from which I could find no outlet. Then again, all was reburied, and I was standing on a grass-covered mound."

An Arab sheik had been dispatched to the nearest village on their arrival, and at dawn he brought back six men who were ready to dig. Before evening they had discovered two palaces much like those Botta had found at Khorsabad. For want of better names Layard called them the Northwest Palace and the Southwest Palace.

"And now scarcely a day passed without some new and important discovery," he wrote. He did not yet know the name of the mighty king into whose domain he now penetrated, but it was the magnificent fortress of Ashurnasirpal, the first king of the Assyrian empire who ruled from 884 to 859 B.C.

One day Layard came upon more than a hundred sculptured slabs "packed in rows, one against the other, and placed in a regular series, according to subject." And not far from the slabs he found a polished black stone sculptured on four sides with twenty small reliefs depicting foreign princes bringing tribute to the Assyrian throne. This is now one of the chief treasures of the British Museum.

He was in the midst of his digging when word came from the local Pasha that he must stop all work at once. The Pasha thought that he was stealing hidden gold. When Layard agreed to work under the watching eye of the Pasha's agent, permission was granted for him to go on. And not a thimbleful of gold was found.

Again the Pasha sent word that he was desecrating holy
ground: Mohammedan graves were there. He even had some
tombstones set up at night, Layard discovered, to give his
contention credibility. Still, a Pasha may not be argued with.

Layard tried to go on digging surreptitiously for a time.
The Pasha seldom rode out that way, and he thought it worth
while to take a chance. He unearthed a beautiful crouching
lion, a pair of damaged winged bulls, and a human figure
nine feet high. But soon he decided that it was too dangerous
to continue the work. He buried these objects in the earth
again and went to visit Rawlinson in Baghdad, but he did not
stay there long. News was brought that the old Pasha was
dead, and the new governor did not object to his excavating.

So Layard went on with his digging, now not only at Nimrud but also at Kuyunjik, where Botta had tried so long and
failed. And Layard's luck was with him again, for he came
upon more palaces. The mound at Kuyunjik contained the
palaces of the later Assyrian kings, of Sennacherib and of his
grandson Ashurbanipal. Layard walked along the endless
corridors and into the lofty chambers, gazed at the war chariots and hunting scenes carved on the alabaster walls, and
realized that this was Nineveh, the great Assyrian city.
Botta had been wrong: he had not found Nineveh at all.

Proof of Layard's conviction that he had in truth found
Nineveh was near at hand. In two large chambers of the
palace he found the Royal Library of Ashurbanipal, the oldest known library in Asia. Here twenty-two thousand clay
tablets inscribed with cuneiform characters lay in confused

heaps on the floor. Layard packed them carefully to send back to England, where they may still be seen in the British Museum.

The inscriptions on those tablets brought the Assyrians back to life again as even their pictures on the miles of sculptured alabaster friezes could not do. Here were the recitals of their conquests and their triumphant wars, and here too were their myths and all the knowledge they had collected in their vigorous lives. The myth of the creation was told here, the tale of the beginnings of all things and of man himself. Here were the myths that sought to explain the mystery of death and of life after death, and of the other problems that no man can explain save through myths. But there was science written on those tablets as well as mythology. Five hundred of the tablets dealt with medicine, giving "good, honest, practical prescriptions for every ill under the sun from earache to the restoration of the drowned."

Some of the tablets dealt with botany: hundreds of plants and their properties were described and names given them. Others dealt with chemistry, for the Assyrians knew the practical use of large numbers of minerals. There were treatises on the making of glass and on glazes for pottery. Scattered among these tablets were some concerning astronomy, indicating a tremendous knowledge of the sun, moon, and stars. And, in addition, the Assyrians were philologists: there were many dictionaries among the heaped-up tablets that Layard had found.

The queer writing on the dusty, broken tablets responded

now to the work of scholars and revived the vigorous life of the Assyrians and the far-reaching knowledge they had attained. Much of that knowledge was forgotten through the centuries; only gradually was it built up again by succeeding generations. Death and forgetfulness — new life and awareness, is the old cycle that has gone on since the world began.

Layard was not content with merely sending cuneiform tablets to England for scholars to read: he wanted the people to realize the magnitude of the Assyrian sculpture. He wanted, in fact, to send back to England some of the colossal figures he had found in Ashurnasirpal's palace at Nimrud.

He realized that their gigantic size would make the statues difficult to ship and planned to have them cut into several pieces for the journey across the Mediterranean. But the British government now ruled that any object too large to be shipped as a whole must be buried in the earth again.

Layard was greatly disappointed at this ruling. He was determined that somehow at least one colossal winged bull and one winged lion must be shown to the people of London. He would use all his ingenuity in finding some way to ship them.

The colossal figures he selected for sending weighed 10 tons apiece. He had them bound carefully in felt to withstand any shocks they might receive. He had no special equipment for hoisting such gigantic stone figures up from the earth, but a gang of half-naked Arab workmen strained and pulled at the ropes, and others poured on water to cool the rope as it smoked and crackled under the strain. A crowd of Bedouins with their camels and horses and some Moslem women from the neighboring village stood watching as the bull was pulled into an erect position and then drawn slowly upward. Layard himself, his beard and long hair blowing in the wind, shouted directions which no one could hear in the confusion, until he threw chunks of sod to attract attention to what he was saying.

In this way, slowly and with prodigious effort, the bull was raised on creaking ropes. Then, in a tense moment, all the ropes broke at once, and the men shouted and the women screamed as the statue dropped in a cloud of dust to a platform on wooden rollers that had been prepared for it. When the dust had cleared it was apparent that no harm had been done.

Now slowly the great bulk of the stone bull was moved out of the mound on the platform, and then pushed and shoved into a waiting cart that would take it along the road toward the river. A group of Arabs escorted it.

The strange procession had not gone far when they were beset by robbers. Bullets were exchanged, one of which hit the bull, and the mark of it may still be seen by visitors to the British Museum. But the robbers were frightened away, and the procession went on to the river.

There, with some difficulty, the bull was loaded on a raft supported on six hundred inflated skins, and the statue floated down the fast-flowing river to the waiting ship that brought it to London.

The whole process was repeated with the winged lion, but

this time Layard was not so fortunate, for the lion was dropped and cracked, and eventually it broke in two.

After the winged bull and the winged lion had been sent on their journeys, Layard went back to the mound, filled in his trenches, and prepared to return to London. There in 1848 he worked on a report of what he had done. The British government appropriated only a very small amount of money for its publication, and, since no artist had been employed, Layard had to illustrate it with his own sketches. Still, the book was widely read. Layard wrote a friend that eight thousand copies of it had been sold in a single year, "which," he said, "will place it side by side with Mrs. Rundell's *Cookery.*"

7.

Ur and Its Unanswered Questions

In the nineteenth century the Assyrians were not the only Mesopotamian people that stirred the archaeologists' interest, nor was Nineveh the only ancient city whose ruins they wanted to uncover. They had read of Babylon with its hanging gardens, the beautiful city where King Nebuchadnezzar II ruled in the sixth century B.C. Its site could be located with some assurance: it had stood on the east bank of the rushing Euphrates River and nearer to the Persian Gulf than Nine-

veh. Hormuzd Rassam, Layard's assistant, had been the first
to excavate there and had found some valuable clay tablets.
But it was Robert Koldewey, the talented German archaeologist, who in the early twentieth century uncovered the
deeply buried city.

Babylon was a walled city with many gates: the Ishtar
Gate, the greatest one, was said to be made of bronze. The
streets of Babylon were wide and partly paved, and one
broad avenue that led from the royal palace to the temple
tower was lined on either side with high walls, decorated in
bright-colored glazed brick to depict a procession of yellow
lions walking toward the temple.

It seemed almost certain, however, that another far older
city must lie beneath the ruins of Nebuchadnezzar's capital
— the city of King Hammurabi, who ruled probably in the
second millennium before Christ. Scholars knew of the importance of this king. A stone slab inscribed with his laws,
the oldest code of laws in the world, had been found as far
away as Susa in Elam, for he had evidently ruled a wide
empire. In addition, a large number of his records and
letters had been found, and scholars were already working
on them. It was known that Babylon was his capital, but
where was King Hammurabi's Babylon now? Archaeologists
from many countries had searched for it without success,
until a clay tablet found at Nineveh revealed its fate. The
Babylon that Hammurabi established had been totally destroyed by Sennacherib, who with ruthless vengeance had
obliterated all traces of the city.

In 1922 the English archaeologist Charles Leonard Woolley, who headed a group sent out by the British Museum and the University of Pennsylvania, began to investigate the site of an even more ancient city than the older Babylon — one that was farther south, and still nearer to the Persian Gulf. This was the site of Ur, which had flourished long before the time of Hammurabi's Babylon. It was built, Woolley estimated, about thirty-five hundred years before Christ, in the country of Sumer close to the head of the Persian Gulf.

Legend knew this ancient city as "Ur of the Chaldees." It was said to have been the first city established after the Creation, the home of the Jewish Abraham, the center of the world's first empire. There were many references to it in the Old Testament, but the city eventually disappeared under drifts of sand, and its site was long forgotten.

As early as 1854 the British consul at Basra in Mesopotamia discovered the place where Ur had stood. He found an inscribed clay cylinder which when it was deciphered announced that a Babylonian king had restored the "ziggurat," or temple tower here about 550 B.C. Some mounds where the city had been could still be seen in the wastes of sand, but no men were here, no life save for an occasional hungry jackal.

After the First World War was over, Leonard Woolley and his party went to work in this sandy waste. They dug down into a rubbish heap that lay at the base of the tallest mound and found some ancient graves. Then, driving a shaft down through the sandy soil they came upon a hard bank of clay. The clay was smooth, clean, apparently water-laid, and it was 8 feet thick. Clay like this had not been laid in a series of strata at different times: it had all been laid at once. Only the waters of a great flood could have made this bank of clay. The diggers sank their shaft down through the clay and came upon a primitive settlement.

It was the original Ur, and life there had stopped when the waters of a great flood covered it with mud. That flood, scholars believe, may be identical with the Biblical deluge in the story of Noah. One of the Sumerian legends tells a similar tale about how Ut-Napishthim was warned by the gods in time to build an ark so that he survived the flood. The myth was preserved in the records of Ashurbanipal's Royal Assyrian Library, and the cuneiform inscription had been deciphered by a young man at the British Museum, who marveled at the resemblance this legend bore to the Biblical narrative.

Six days and nights
Raged wind, deluge and storm upon the earth,
When the seventh day arrived the storm ceased
Which had fought like a host of men:
The sea was calm, hurricane and deluge ceased.

I beheld the land and cried aloud:
For the whole of mankind were turned to clay;
Hedged fields had become marshes.
I opened a window and the light fell upon my face. . . .

When the seventh day arrived,
I brought forth a dove and let it go.
The dove went to and fro:
As there was no resting place it turned back.
I brought forth a raven and let it go.
The raven went and saw the decrease of the waters.
It ate, it waded, it croaked (?), it turned not back. . . .

I offered sacrifice . . . .

The gods smelt the savor,
The gods smelt the goodly savor.
The gods gathered like flies over the sacrifice.

After the flood, the Sumerians had rebuilt and established other cities, such as Kish and Erech, which have not yet been fully explored.

By 3500 B.C. Ur was a lively place, its people filled with enterprising new ideas. They traded with the cities along the Indus River and may even have done business with the Far East. Indian beads and Chinese pottery were among the strange objects the archaeologists unearthed.

Was it the energy of a people whose past had been obliterated and who were starting life again, that made them accomplish so much? Was it sheer genius? Whatever it was, the achievements of these people were amazing.

They organized a government and collected enough in taxes to build a grand canal and a series of smaller canals leading into it. On these canals the barges carried the products of the surrounding country, to be unloaded at the quaysides and stored in great warehouses. And a system of irrigation ditches was constructed for the benefit of the farmers whose produce supported the dwellers of the town.

Besides all this, the Sumerians invented the cuneiform system of writing. Assyrians, Babylonians, and Persians all wrote in this special script and modified the cuneiform characters to suit themselves — but the Sumerians were first. Their scribes recorded their business transactions in wedge-shaped characters on damp clay tablets. Soon they found other uses for their writing besides mere business records. They composed stories and epic poems such as the story of the flood. This was the world's first literature.

Government, business, and literature were only a part of the accomplishment of the extraordinary people who built their new city of Ur on the ancient site. The Sumerians were the first to make systematic astronomical observations. They invented a remarkable number system and developed a primitive algebra. They knew metallurgy and were skilled craftsmen in silver and gold, in copper and tin. They fashioned jewelery set with such stones as carnelian, lapis lazuli, diorite, and obsidian. They knew how to manufacture glass, pottery, and glazes, drugs and cosmetics, paints, perfumes, and beer. One scholar has listed twenty-five different things which the Sumerians were the first to discover. In Ur the archaeologists uncovered evidence of all these things as they dug through the drifting sand.

Gradually, with patient excavating, Leonard Woolley and those with him unearthed houses, palaces, and markets from the earth. The most impressive of these was the brick temple tower called a ziggurat which they found in the tallest mound. The "Mountain of God," as the Sumerians called it, had been built by King Ur-Nammu four hundred years before the Jewish leader Abraham was born, and was dedicated to the moon god. It was a very large building measuring 210 feet in length and 140 feet in breadth, and it was solidly constructed of burnt brick. On every brick the name of Ur-Nammu, the king, was imprinted. The ziggurat had a high, flat top, and three stairways led to its summit. There a jeweled sanctuary was set among waving palm trees. The sanctuary and the palm trees are gone now, but the stairways still lead up to the summit where the king who was the moon god once held communion with the goddess of the moon.

The rites and ceremonies at the ziggurat must have been impressive on those nights when the white moonlight shone down on the roofs of the city and on the jeweled sanctuary atop the "Mountain of God." There the triple stairways seem made for magnificent processions of priests, and the great courtyard at the temple's base was a fitting place for ceremonies.

That great courtyard had another use besides the ceremonial, for the king was a landowner as well as a god, and to this courtyard his tenants came to pay their taxes. There was no coined money: they brought what was his due in goods. Cattle, sheep, and goats were brought here, sacks of grain, jars of oil, casks of beer, wheels of cheese, pots of butter and bundles of wood; all these were handed to the king's agents, while scribes made records of what they had received on duplicate clay tablets. One tablet was handed to the taxpayer; the other was kept to be filed in the temple archives.

It may be that the Sumerians had once lived in a mountainous country, and to remind themselves of this, perhaps, they had built the ziggurat on the level plain of the Mesopotamian valley. However that may be, it had great fame among all the valley people. In time many copies of it were made. One of the most famous is the Tower of Babel which is described in the Old Testament.

But the ziggurat, with its ceremonial stairways and its courtyard, and the houses and other buildings were not the only finds that Woolley made, or even the most important ones. The Royal Graves of Ur were soon to display treasures of blazing gold whose magnificence astonished the world.

The Sumerians believed in immortality; like many other peoples they buried their dead with all the trappings that might be useful in the future life. Many of the graves, therefore, bore rich collections of jewelry and furniture. In some countries, even though attempts had been made to keep them secret, such collections had been looted by grave robbers. In Ur, however, no one had disturbed the graves through all the years until Leonard Woolley and his co-workers came there.

There were two graves of women, indeed of queens, who probably had been buried in about 3300 B.C.

A shaft had been dug down to a depth of about 30 feet to the burial chamber of one of these queens. A stone arch covered this grave chamber. Under the arch there had once been a wooden ceiling, but this had collapsed and fallen on the bodies of five people who lay there. One of these was Queen Shub-Ab. The other four were apparently her servants.

The queen had been beautifully arrayed for burial. She wore a rich and delicate headdress which had seven golden ribbons that radiated from the center of her head and were interlaced with gold poplar leaves. Around her neck she wore gold chains and strings of carnelian beads, and on her ears finely wrought gold earrings. There were a number of gold rings on her fingers, and near her hand was a fluted golden cup whose workmanship is said by connoisseurs never to have been surpassed, even by the famous goldsmiths of the Italian Renaissance.

An engraved gold cylinder seal was found near the queen. The design inscribed on this seal showed men carrying offerings, and one of the offerings was a lyre whose sounding board was ornamented with a bull's head of hammered gold. This was significant, for the Sumerian Moon God was called "the Young Bull of Heaven." The crescent of the bull's horns was the king's symbol.

The bones of sacrificed sheep lay in a section of the grave chamber that had later been filled with earth. There was evidence of a funerary feast in the upper strata of the shaft.

Queen Shub-Ab was richly decked and mysterious in her chamber, but the second grave was stranger still. This also was a shaft grave. A ramp led down to it about 27 feet below the surface of the earth. And here were not five, but seventy-four bodies. Sixty-eight of these were the bodies of women; the other six were men, who apparently had served as body-guards. Splendid treasures were buried with these bodies, and jewelry lay so thick upon the floor that walking across it was like walking on a carpet of gold.

The women lay in ordered rows — there was no confusion, no sign of violence. Each woman wore an elaborate head-dress of gold. These must have lain very heavy on their heads, for there was still dark, powdery evidence that the women had worn wigs beneath the gold. The six men lay in a row at one end of the chamber.

There apparently had been a canopy or tent in one corner of the chamber, the cloth of which, of course, had long since disappeared. But there remained as evidence traces of the supporting wooden poles that had been overlaid with silver and a central pole inlaid with shell, red sandstone, and silver plating, and gold bands alternating with shell rings. Probably a funeral dance had once been held under this canopy, for a number of musical instruments lay beside it. One of these was a lyre richly ornamented with gold, silver, and mosaic. Its wood and strings had long since crumbled to dust, but with great skill and care it was possible to re-construct the instrument from the outlines the metal and mosaic had left in the dust. This lyre, like the one on the cylinder seal found in Queen Shub-Ab's grave, had a handsome bull's head of hammered gold with eyes made of shell and lapis lazuli. This has been described as the "finest sculptured head of its kind ever unearthed as a product of the ancient world."

Many and strange were the ornaments and furnishings buried with the queen in this grave, but strangest, perhaps, was a pair of rams portrayed as standing on their hind legs while browsing in a golden thicket. They were beautifully and intricately made. Their bodies were covered with a fleece of shell; their manes, beards, and horns were of lapis lazuli, and their heads and legs were of gold. No one knows the significance of these figures.

There are, in fact, a great many things about these royal graves in Ur that we cannot understand. It is easy to list the golden objects and to marvel at them; it is very hard to find out what they mean. What ceremonies accompanied the queen to that still burial chamber? Had the sixty-eight women marched in and laid themselves down of their own will? Where was the king? No one yet has been able to guess.

8.

The Forgotten Hittites

The archaeologists with their digging had brought to light several different peoples who once had lived in the fertile land between the Tigris and the Euphrates Rivers. But it must not be thought that these people tilled their fields and carried on their commerce without interference from the neighboring world. They had enemies on every side who attacked and tried to destroy them again and again. Among their most persistent foes were the dreaded Hittites, who came into Asia Minor and Syria some time about 1900 B.C.

The story of the Hittites is a strange one. They were a powerful force in the world for centuries and ruled over vassal princes of many petty kingdoms. They were a terror to all who opposed them, yet they vanished and were completely forgotten as if they had never existed at all. Then, after all the unheeding centuries, the archaeologists succeeded in uncovering their story.

Readers of the Old Testament had known the name of the Hittites for generations. The Bible relates that when the Children of Israel entered the Promised Land the Hittites were living there, that Esau's wife was a Hittite, and that King Solomon had Hittite wives. The Bible says further that Solomon sold horses, which he imported from Egypt, to the "Kings of the Hittites." The Syrian army was so afraid of its Hittite enemies that when the Syrians heard the noises of horses and chariots "they said to one another, Lo, the King of Israel hath hired against us the Kings of the Hittites and the Kings of the Egyptians. . . . Wherefore they rose and fled into the twilight."

But these brief suggestions are all the Bible tells about this mysterious people, who remained an enigma until late in the nineteenth century, when scholars began to work on the puzzle.

The solution to the mystery had its beginning in 1876 when Archibald Henry Sayce, a British scholar, read a paper to the Society of Biblical Archaeology. He told of several basalt blocks that were inscribed with a peculiar writing. This looked something like Egyptian hieroglyphics, but it was not the same, and he could not tell what the inscriptions meant. Some of these stone slabs had been found in a corner of the bazaar in Hamath, Syria; others had been built into the walls of houses there. The townspeople were very superstitious about them and tried to prevent anyone from making copies of them, but the Pasha of Turkey removed five of these stones and put them in the Museum at Constantinople. An English missionary succeeded in getting a plaster cast of one, which he sent to the British Museum.

The Hamath Stones were not the only ones bearing the curious inscriptions; a similar stone had been built into the wall of a mosque at Aleppo in Syria. People believed that this stone had power to cure eye diseases, and the constant rubbing of eyelids against the stone had worn it almost smooth, although the inscription on it was still clear. It too bore "small figures and signs which appear to be a kind of hieroglyphic writing, though it does not resemble that of Egypt."

These were the stones which Sayce described to the members of the Society of Biblical Archaeology. He maintained that they had been inscribed by the Hittites of whom the Bible spoke. The Society thought his theory completely unfounded.

But now the same "small figures and signs" that had been seen on the Hamath and Aleppo stones began to turn up in more distant places. They were found on a rock carving at Ivriz, which is in the Taurus Mountains of Asia Minor, and with some excitement travelers reported that they found them also at Alaja Hüyük within the bend of the Halys River and near the little Turkish village of Bogazköy.

At Bogazköy there were also the ruins of what appeared to have once been a fortified city. In the very middle of these ruins a much-weathered stone bore the same curious marks, and about two miles away on the surface of a great rock wall they appeared again. This time the inscription was accompanied by pictures: a double procession of figures sculptured in high relief. The men in the carving marched along wearing helmets, short-belted tunics, and shoes turned up at the toes, and they seemed to have large noses.

Who had built that ancient fortress? Who had inscribed these strange characters on the rocks that were scattered in such widespread places? Who were these men in helmets with their large noses and shoes with turned-up toes? If they were indeed the Hittites, as Sayce insisted, then who, after all, were the Hittites? A riddle, a mystery, an unknown quantity.

Some reality was given these mysterious people when a group of clay tablets was unearthed in 1887 at Tel-el-Am-arna on the bank of the Nile about 200 miles above Cairo. These cuneiform tablets were written in the Babylonian, or Akkadian, language that apparently was used at that time as the language of diplomacy and commerce. When the tablets were deciphered, they were found to be correspond-ence between the Pharaoh Ikhnaton and the great kings of Babylonia and Assyria and other neighboring states. Among them were some letters from the king of the Hittites. One congratulated Ikhnaton on his accession to the throne.

After the Amarna letters were found, the Hittites were no

longer shadowy, mysterious figures who had left inscriptions on scattered stone slabs but actual people who had corresponded with the Pharaohs of Egypt.

It was to be more than sixty years, however, before scholars succeeded in deciphering the Hittite hieroglyphs described by Sayce at the Society of Biblical Archaeology. The English scholars were particularly interested in these. The German Hittitologists, as they were called, worked especially hard at the Hittite cuneiform script, which, though written in Babylonian characters, was a completely different language from that of the Babylonians or the Assyrians.

It was the Germans who succeeded first. In 1906 Dr. Hugo Winckler made an important find at Bogazköy. He was excavating inside the ruined fortress when he came upon a row of store chambers that seemed to have been destroyed by some great conflagration. Pushing into the debris on the floor of these, he came to heaps of inscribed clay tablets that had been baked and hardened by the fire. He found a total of about ten thousand tablets, which were the royal archives of a Hittite king. Some of the tablets were in the same cuneiform writing that had puzzled scholars for so long, but many were in the Akkadian used by the Babylonians and Assyrians in their business transactions. Winckler was able to decipher all the Akkadian tablets, but those in the Hittite language remained illegible.

In 1915 the archaeologists were able to take another step forward. In that year a Czech named Friedrich Hrozny found that he could make a Hittite grammar with the cuneiform characters he deciphered. The grammar showed that Hittite was an Indo-European language; these people must have come, like other Europeans, from the Indo-Iranian plateau. Apparently they were not related in any way to the dwellers of Mesopotamia or of Egypt.

So far, so good. But still the Hittite hieroglyphics were unread. Then in 1947 the Karatepe Stone was found by the German scholar Helmuth T. Bossert of the University of Istanbul. And just as the Rosetta Stone had made the reading of Egyptian hieroglyphics possible, so now the Karatepe Stone provided the key to the Hittite hieroglyphics, as its inscriptions were bilingual.

With a number of Turkish assistants Bossert had been investigating a mound on the Karatepe, or "Black Mountain," in the Taurus range of southeastern Turkey. Beneath the summit of this mound was a fortress which had two entrance buildings, one to the north and one to the south. Long corridors led to each building, and each corridor was flanked with inscribed slabs. The inscription on the left wall of each corridor was in Phoenician, that on the wall facing it, in Hittite hieroglyphics. The inscriptions on the opposite walls were not identical, but they were similar enough to provide a clue for deciphering the unknown language. The Hittite hieroglyphics that had baffled scholars so long could at last be read, or at least a good part of them was legible. Some of the hieroglyphs have not yet been deciphered.

Now, although scholars are still unable to understand all the little pictographs, enough of both Hittite cuneiform and Hittite hieroglyphic has been deciphered to make it possible to reconstruct most of their history.

Some time after 1900 B.C. they had fought their way into Asia Minor from the east and settled down in small groups, bringing their wives and families with them. In the mountains and valleys of Asia Minor they had settled down in separate tribes, farming and trading with their neighbors. Apparently, in about 1800 B.C., a man named Annitas had conquered several of the valley tribes, and he boasted that their cities were utterly destroyed and declared accursed. By the end of his reign he probably controlled all the central plateau.

No one is quite sure, however, who this Annitas was or whether he was a Hittite.

A much more authentic figure, who lived in the mid-seventeenth century B.C., was King Labarnas, from whom later Hittites claimed their descent. One of his successors writes thus of him:

"Formerly Labarnas was king; and then his sons, his brothers, his connections by marriage and his blood-relations were united. And the land was small; but wherever he marched to battle, he subdued the lands of his enemies with might. He destroyed the lands and made them powerless, and he made the seas his frontiers. And when he returned from battle, his sons went each to every part of the land, to Hupisna, to Tuwanuwa, to Nenassa, to Lānda, to Zallara, to Parsuhanda and to Lusna, and governed the land, and the great cities of the land were assigned to them."

Strange forgotten names those cities had, but the record shows how Labarnas extended his kingdom. He was so strong that his very name became synonymous with that of king. After he had united all the nearby city-states under his rule, he succeeded in establishing the right of succession to his son. This kingdom was called the "Land of Hatti" and the great fortress at Bogazköy was its capital.

Hattusilis I was Labarnas' son, and he was strong as his father had been. He extended the kingdom as far as Aleppo in northern Syria.

Labarnas' grandson, Mursilis I, who was next in succession, went even further. In mad, surprising raids, he pushed his army all the way down the Euphrates and must have astonished even himself by raiding the great city of Babylon. Mursilis came home from that expedition with trains of donkeys carrying the loot, and he marched through the streets of the Hittite capital, Hattusas, and up to his palace while the crowds cheered. He had changed the land of Hatti into an empire equal in strength to that of Egypt or of Babylonia. He was murdered in 1590 B.C.

The Hittite Empire extended over all Asia Minor and Syria. Caravan routes connected each of its cities with one another, and in all these cities the people paid tribute to the king and were conscripted into his armies. But though all the conquered people were part of this great kingdom, they continued to speak their own languages: eight different languages were spoken in the Hittite Empire, and there were eight different sets of gods. Over all these gods reigned "Teshub, the Weather God," and he was lord of winds, storms, lightning, and thunder. The Hittite king was known to be helped by this Teshub: he assumed as part of his title "Favorite of the Weather God." One of the Hittite kings wrote, "And the gods stood by me, the proud storm god, my lord." And another, "The goddess, my lady, always held me by the hand."

The Hittites were warriors skilled in the ways of war, but they were not very good artists. The sculptured figures found on the rocks in so many places are very crudely done. Still, they bring back in their rough way the images of men who once lived, fought, and ruled. There is, for instance, the carved figure of a warrior who guards the King's Gate at Bogazköy. He wears a belted kilt and a helmet, and carries a short sword and a battle ax. The helmet is plumed and has ear pieces, with a kind of pigtail hanging down at the back of the neck. The sword and battle ax were probably made of iron, for the Hittites were the first to use this metal for weapons and tools.

Formidable though fighters like this one must have been, the real strength of the Hittite army lay in its horse-drawn chariots. The Hittites had learned horse breeding from the Hurrians, a people of Asiatic origin who had formed the kingdom of the Mitanni in the lower Mesopotamian Valley. And the Hittites used their horses not for transportation but for war. The chariots they drove into battle were light, with spoked wheels, and so constructed that they could carry two men, one to drive the horse, the other to fight.

With iron weapons, and horse-drawn war chariots, it was not long before the Hittite armies were the terror of all the neighboring country, and their kings knew how to take advantage of their conquests. One tablet that Winckler found is a challenge from a Hittite king to the ruler of the province of Arzawa, which lies on the western coast of Asia Minor. It reads: "My subjects went over to you. When I demanded them back from you, you did not restore them to me; and you called me a child and made light of me. Up then! Let us fight, and let the storm god, my lord, decide the case."

The King of Arzawa must have regretted his recklessness, for the tablet goes on: "And when I had conquered the whole land of Arzawa, the number of civilian captives that I, My Majesty, brought back to the royal palace was altogether 66,000; but what the lords, the soldiers and the charioteers of Hattusas brought back in the way of civilian captives, oxen, and sheep — there was no way of counting. And when I had conquered the whole land of Arzawa, I returned home to Hattusas."

In about 1375 B.C. when the Hittite King Suppiluliumas was crowned, his empire was so powerful that it was accepted as a great power by the world's most influential leaders, and they were anxious to make alliances with him.

The widow of the Egyptian Pharaoh Tutankhamen, for example, wrote, "My husband is dead, and I have no son. But thy sons they say are many. If thou wilt send me a son of thine, he shall become my husband."

This proposal was not immediately accepted and a second letter made the same request. The boy was sent but he was killed near the Egyptian border; no one knows what happened to the lonely widow.

Relations between the Egyptians and the Hittites were not always harmonious. Early in the thirteenth century B.C., the Pharaoh Rameses II declared war on the king of the Hittites. Their armies met on the bank of the Orontes River in northern Syria, and twenty thousand men fought on each side. The encounter was nearly a disaster for Rameses, because he was overconfident and the Hittites were great strategists. But a truce was finally called and a peace treaty signed. The terms of the treaty were engraved on a silver plate, and they pledged brotherhood and peace between the two nations "for all time." After the signing Rameses married the daughter of Hattusilis III, then king of the Hittites. Her name was Ma'atne-frure, which meant "Truth is the beauty of Re."

So year after year the armies marched out of the great fortress at Bogazköy, the terror of all who dared to oppose them. And what happened to them then? The tablets do not explain. It is known that the Assyrians ravaged their cities — had their kings grown too weak to oppose them? And hordes of barbarians from the forests beyond the Danube and from the grasslands across the Caucasus swept down in successive raids. The great capital city Hattusas was ravaged and burned. It was never rebuilt.

That was the story that was gradually pieced together from the tablets that Winckler had found. And this was the discovery of the people who for many centuries had been forgotten.

Today archaeologists from England and America, from Germany and France, and not least of all from Turkey itself, are working to fill in the outlines of the Hittites' story. And while they dig, trying to put the pieces of their tale together, the question arises: Why were the Hittites forgotten so long? They were strong. They had great powers of organization, great faith that the weather god was on their side. Were these things not enough? If they had had a talent for architecture, or had been skilled craftsmen or poets, would their memory have survived in the slow-moving stream of time?

It is easy to assume that if the Hittites had put their energy into something more durable than war their memory might have survived. Yet this is not necessarily true. For on the other side of the world in Central America the Mayas were great architects and craftsmen, but they, too, were forgotten — perhaps because of the ruthless Spanish conquest.

9.

Mr. Stephens, Mr. Catherwood, and
the Mayas

The shop of "Bartlett and Welford, Antiquarian Booksellers," stood on lower Broadway in New York, opposite the City Hall, and to it one morning in 1838 came John Lloyd Stephens, an elegantly dressed young lawyer with a mass of reddish whiskers and dark, luminous eyes. A man-about-town, often seen sipping iced brandy at Delmonico's, or riding his spirited horse along Broadway, Stephens had been to Egypt, Greece, and Turkey and had written an account of his travels in a book that was widely popular.

The senior partner of the booksellers' establishment and the young author were good friends; in fact it was John R.

Bartlett who first suggested to Stephens that he take another journey and write another book. Their conversation was recorded afterward in Bartlett's journal.

"Why do you not undertake the exploration of Yucatán and Central America?" he asked Stephens that morning. "There is a field that is quite unexplored where there are numerous objects of interest in ruined cities, temples, and other works of art."

Bartlett writes, "Mr. Stephens said he had never heard of these remains and would be glad to know more about them. I invited him to my house, where I showed him Waldeck's work on Yucatán, a beautiful work in folio . . . which I had imported from Paris."

That was how Stephens' interest in the ruins of Central America started. He turned the pages of the book which Bartlett showed him, and his interest mounted. It had been written in Spanish by Capitán Antonio del Río, who had visited the ruins in 1786 by order of the Spanish king. The captain wore a tri-corner hat on the expedition and a powdered periwig, while the latest fashionable perfume spread through the tropical forest round him. Thus arrayed, he had cut the vines and roots from the ancient stones and brought them to the light of day for the first time since the jungle had covered them a thousand years before, making some rough pencil sketches as he did so. Jean Frederic Maximilian, Comte de Waldeck, the soldier-artist, had illustrated del Río's account later with romantic engravings. This book was published in Paris in 1822. Waldeck volunteered the information that he thought the ruined structures had been made by descendants of the Egyptians.

This was the first book published on the Central American ruins, and it was this book that lighted Stephens' curiosity. He was not alone in his ignorance of the American Indians, for no one in the United States knew much about them. Indians were regarded merely as half-naked savages. No one then had advanced the theory that ancient ancestors of the American Indians had come from Siberia by slow stages, settling here and there and moving on again. There were a good many who thought in a confused way that the Indians might be Chinese, or Phoenicians, or Egyptians, or that they might be descendants of the Lost Tribes of Israel, or that they had come across the sea from the mythical lost continent of Atlantis. But certainly no one believed that an Indian tribe had built great and beautiful cities in America — cities that had disappeared without a trace, when the jungle growth swallowed them. Savages do not build beautiful cities, the Americans would have said.

Nevertheless, John Lloyd Stephens, turning over the pages of Count Waldeck's book, wanted to see those ruins. After he had studied the engravings, he made up his mind that he would go to see what the jungle had covered. By coincidence, after he had booked passage, the Special Confidential Agent to Central America died, and President Martin Van Buren gave Stephens the post. This official appointment lent him prestige in Central America.

He sailed out of New York Harbor, October 3, 1839, on the

British brig *Mary Ann* headed for Belize in British Honduras. "It was seven o'clock in the morning," he wrote later. "The streets and wharfs were still; the Battery was desolate and at that moment of leaving it on a voyage of uncertain duration, New York seemed more beautiful than I had ever known it before."

Stephens was not traveling alone: his friend Frederick Catherwood, an English architect, was with him. Solidly built, with round face and sandy hair, "Mr. Catherwood," as Stephens always called him, was very formal and restrained in his manner. He had a burning passion for archaeology, however, enormous patience, and a meticulous love of detail. He brought an easel, drawing pads, and pencils with him so that he might record whatever they found.

When Stephens and Catherwood had arrived in the shabby little seaport of Belize, each of them armed himself with a brace of pistols and started on muleback along the trail up Mico Mountain. Their destination was the deserted ruin of Copán which was in Honduras near the border of Guatemala. Their guide carried a sword as well as his pistol, and their chief muleteer had an unsheathed machete in his hand and big jingling spurs on his bare feet.

The road led through a gloomy jungle. White butterflies floated over their heads, tree frogs chirped, and parrots startled them with raucous calls. At frequent intervals the roots of giant mahogany trees made hurdles for the mules.

"For five long hours we were dragged through mud-holes, squeezed in gulleys, knocked against trees and tumbled over roots; every step required great care and great physical exertion. . . . I felt that our inglorious epitaph might be 'Tossed over the head of a mule, brained by the trunk of a mahogany tree, and buried in the mud of Mico Mountain.'" This description is part of an entry in Stephens' diary.

Now they left the jungle and climbed up among fantastic mountain peaks where the ground was covered with enormous candelabra cacti. Then they were in the jungle again, with parrots screaming and howler monkeys swinging in the branches. They passed through a village with a cobbled square and an ancient Spanish church. It seemed to them that all the men, women, and children in the whitewashed houses, were making tortillas, as they could hear the *slap, slap* of the dough on flat stones. And a young woman smiled at them as they pushed on along the ancient road that skirts the Río Copán.

So at last Stephens stood at the edge of that tropical river looking through a curtain of vines and flowering orchids, and saw a massive wall half-covered by the jungle growth. Here were the ruins of the Mayan city of Copán.

Stephens crossed the river and entered the ruined city, making his way slowly through the jungle growth, and stood in the central courtyard of a great stone building. Long-armed, black spider monkeys were its only inhabitants. Nearby he saw the ruins of an amphitheater, a majestic staircase guarded by two stone jaguars, a strange pyramid with a flattened top — and all these were covered with twisting roots and vines so that he could only vaguely distinguish their outlines. In the courtyard in which he stood there were fourteen stone slabs, or "steles," each one taller than a man. He found that each slab, when he had disentangled the vines and roots from it, was covered with intricate and elaborate carving. On its front and back faces there were strange heads, plumed birds, coiling serpents, leaves and flowers. But on the sides of the steles mysterious hieroglyphs had been carved; he could not read them.

He did not know the name of this city he had found, or when it had been built, or why it had been deserted. "I am entering abruptly on new ground," he wrote.

He was eager to start work there at once. He wanted to hire workers with spades, mattocks, and ladders to pull away the choking jungle vines. He sought out the local dictator, Don Gregorio, for help.

Don Gregorio had flowing mustaches and a threatening air. He could not understand why anyone should want to investigate the old carved stones which he called "idols." He thought the newcomers must be up to some trick. Perhaps Stephens and Catherwood planned to upset the Honduras government.

Just as this interview was coming to a climax, the owner of the property on which the ruins stood appeared with the title deed to the land in his hand. He was José María, a quiet-spoken man in clean white cotton shirt and pantaloons. In conversation it now developed that his wife was sick. Catherwood had a little cabinet filled with English medicines; some of these might help her. So they went across the river to the house of José María with its corn-husk roof, and after they had seen his wife were glad to be invited to stay there.

Lying in his hammock that night, wreathed in the smoke of an excellent cigar which José María had given him, Stephens made excited plans. No one now should question his right to examine the ruins, for he would buy them: the land on which they stood would be his.

In the morning José María seemed pleased with the idea of the sale. But Don Gregorio appeared and interfered with the transaction. José María hesitated. It looked as if the whole plan might fall through.

Then Stephens took out his passport with its flaming-red seal. And when this did not seem to be quite sufficient, he told them he was a representative of the United States government. Not for nothing had President Van Buren appointed him his Special Confidential Agent. To prove what he said, he pulled out of a bag his diplomatic coat with its array of big brass buttons and put it on. "I had on a Panama hat, soaked with rain and spotted with mud, a check shirt, white pantaloons, yellow up to the knees with mud," he said afterward.

Thus clad, the Special Confidential Agent paraded up and down the mud floor of José María's little house. And José María was impressed, and the sale went through. Stephens paid $50 for Copán.

In the rain next morning they started to work. It was November 17, 1839. They felled the tall trees with axes and cleared the underbrush with machetes. Then they set up poles, hanging their straw hats on them to mark where the poles stood, strung lines from pole to pole and measured, and so at last they mapped the city of Copán. On the map they marked where the great court of the palace was located, and what its dimensions were, and they marked the site of the flat-topped pyramid, and the location of a walled enclosure which they thought later was a sacred ball court.

When the map was finished, Stephens went on cutting and hacking the jungle growth in search of temples and monuments, taking notes as he went. But Catherwood set up his easel and began to make drawings of the ruined buildings and the curiously carved stones. He found that trying to reproduce the carvings on the stones was very difficult, for though he was a skilled artist and had done much sketching in Italy, Greece, and Egypt, these carvings were like nothing he had seen before. He made several unsuccessful attempts; it seemed as if the sculptors who had first conceived these strange carvings were standing behind him, mocking him. Even the monkeys in the branches over his head seemed to be laughing, and the toucans chattered in an irritating way. Swarms of insects flew round him as he worked, so that finally he put on gloves. He found it very hard to draw in gloves.

Gradually, however, he began to appreciate the power of the unknown Mayan artist. Certainly, he said to himself, the carver had had complete mastery of his material. With a kind of savage richness he had filled every inch of the space on the stone with flowers, birds, branches, snakes, and waving plumes. Catherwood had never seen designs like these.

He worked on and his admiration mounted. Here was extraordinary beauty of design, he realized. Deftly he traced each curve and measured each shadow, and slowly he made the partially obliterated patterns live again.

He also reproduced with meticulous care the pebble-shaped hieroglyphics that were carved on the sides of the steles. Stephens, watching him as he worked, was baffled at the strange writing. He said, "I could hardly doubt that [Copán's] history was graven on its monuments." But he could not read that history.

After they had explored Copán, Stephens and Catherwood went on to the ruins of Palenque in the Tumbala Mountains of Mexico. It was a hard journey, for heat and swarming insects did not spare them. After what seemed like many days of traveling, they were pushing wearily through the jungle and wondering what they might find in this new place, when they noticed a number of sculptured stones set in the midst of the jungle. Shortly thereafter they heard one of the Indians at the head of their party crying, "The palace, signor! The palace!"

Then they stopped and looked across a sea of jungle, and saw the palace hanging on the edge of a steep escarpment, the roots of strangler fig trees clambering over its thick walls. Lost, overgrown, without a name, Palenque had withstood the smothering embrace of the jungle for a thousand years before they came.

They took the palace at Palenque for their living quarters, walked through its many chambers, and marveled at a

stuccoed frieze crumbled by time but still brightly colored, where serpents seemed to battle with headless gods. At night they lay awake in the darkness listening to the chanting of tree frogs and wondering when and how and by whom this palace had been built. And next morning under the gray-green moss on the palace wall, they found the same strange glyphs again that they had seen at Copán.

Stephens was bitten by little insects called *niguas* at Palenque; his leg swelled to twice its size. And Catherwood was taken with a fever, but he worked on anyway. The rain was teeming down, but he made a kind of shelter for his drawing pad and kept on drawing, fascinated by the beauty of the strange designs which were so foreign to him.

When they reached Uxmal, which is about 50 miles from Mérida, the capital of Yucatán, Catherwood was too sick to go to the ruins, so Stephens went without him.

"To my astonishment," Stephens said, "I came at once upon a huge open field strewed with mounds of ruins and vast buildings on terraces, and pyramidal structures, grand and in good preservation, richly ornamented, without a bush to obscure the view. . . ."

"Stephens, you are romancing!" Catherwood said when he told him what he had seen. But he managed to pull himself together, to go out to the ruins, to set up his easel, and start to sketch what has since been called by archaeologists the "House of the Dwarfs." His head was pounding, his fever mounting, and it was not long before he collapsed beside his unfinished drawing.

Stephens, "with great apprehensions for his health," arranged to bring "Mr. Catherwood" back to Havana and then to New York. And, carefully, he brought back, too, the drawings Catherwood had made.

Back in the United States in 1840 there was a hard-pressed fight for the Presidency between Martin Van Buren and William Henry Harrison. But despite all the excitement of the presidential election, there was a great stir about the Mayan finds. William Cullen Bryant, the poet and editor of the New York *Evening Post*, saw Catherwood's sepia drawings and praised them highly. The two-volume work called *Incidents of Travel in Central America, Chiapas and Yucatán* with Stephens' text and Catherwood's drawings went into twelve editions in three months.

The two men were back in Central America in 1842. They passed from village to village, from ruin to ruin, and came at last to Chichén Itzá, the largest ruined city of the Maya Empire, and the best preserved. "Ever since we left home, we had our eyes on this place," Stephens said.

He had now seen the ruins of forty different Mayan cities, but none of them impressed him as did Chichén Itzá. Its buildings stood, white and dazzling, under the hot sun; its flat-topped pyramid rose 100 feet above the jungle-covered plain; the walls of its temples were covered with brightly painted bas-reliefs in which Indians with headdresses of waving quetzal feathers seemed to be performing rites of some kind.

Walking through the ruined city and admiring one beautifully built structure after another, he came on one whose use he could not understand. It was a paved rectangular space more than 400 feet long, surrounded by high walls. He was standing in the middle of this court and looking up at the walls when he noticed two massive stone rings, opposite each other and about 20 feet above the ground. Around the place where each ring was secured to the wall two fiercely entwined snakes were carved in a beautiful design. Looking at the rings Stephens now remembered that he had seen similar ones at Uxmal. It must be a ball court, he thought to himself, and he wrote in his journal later, "I shall call it, as occasion requires, the Gymnasium or Tennis Court." He did not know of the game of "jai alai," which the Mexicans still play.

Everywhere he looked, as Stephens studied the carvings at Chichén Itzá, he found illegible hieroglyphics. When he and Catherwood examined them carefully it was clear that they were very much like the ones they had seen at Copán, at Uxmal, at Palenque, and at many other ruins. "Their general character is the same," he wrote. The people of all these cities must certainly have had some connection.

But, though he longed to read the writing that was carved into those stones, to find out the history of the men who had built these cities and to know what had become of them, he could never do it.

Not until about twenty years after Stephens' death were the mysterious hieroglyphics deciphered, and then only a third of them could be read. The key to the interpretation of the Mayan hieroglyphics was discovered in a book written by

Diego de Landa, the second Spanish bishop of Yucatán. In 1566 de Landa had tried to destroy every vestige of Mayan civilization because he considered it heathen. The Mayas had written their history in a large library of documents and de Landa had had all these collected and burned in the public square at Mani. The stone carvings were too big and clumsy to destroy, so he had left them.

There was a strange contradiction in Bishop de Landa's acts, however. For though he burned all the Mayan books, he was still interested in Mayan culture. He made friends with one of the priests and found out all he could from him. Then he wrote a book of his own about the Mayas. Bishop de Landa's book was called *Account of Things in Yucatán,* and in it there were sketches of the hieroglyphics for the twenty days of the Mayan month and for the eighteen months of the Mayan year. This was the key. For Bishop de Landa's book was later found in the Royal Academy of History in Madrid, and with it scholars were able to interpret some of the hieroglyphics.

And now as scholars studied the carvings on the steles of the ruined Mayan cities, a curious fact emerged. The stones were covered not with names of kings and facts of history, but simply with numbers and dates. The Mayas apparently had been obsessed with the passage of time. They had set up a new stone slab and carved it with a date about every twenty years. Studying the Mayan dates, scholars could tell about when each city had been built, when it had been abandoned, and when the whole Mayan Empire had ended.

The first date found on any of the monuments was 68 A.D. according to our calendar. After that one city after another was built, flourished for a time, and was abandoned. The last date found was between 530 and 629 A.D. Then the Mayas disappeared from their ancient cities; they probably migrated north to Yucatán and mingled with the Toltecs and Aztecs there.

No one knows exactly why they built their cities, only to abandon them. Perhaps they practiced wrong farming methods and moved on when the land ceased to support them. Perhaps there was some other reason. But in those years when their great cities flourished, the years when the Europeans were living in what we now call the Dark Ages, these Indians developed one of the greatest civilizations the world has known. They were artists, sculptors, and architects, as great as the Greeks or Romans or Egyptians. They developed a calendar, based on astronomical observation, more accurate, though more complex, than the Gregorian calendar we use today. They had a number system based on units of twenty that was equally original and accurate.

But all these achievements were discovered only very slowly by the men of later times. For until recently only the most hardy archaeologists dared to penetrate the jungle where the Mayan ruins lay. There was one, an Englishman named Alfred P. Maudslay, who read Stephens' *Incidents of Travel* and went into the Central American jungle in 1882. He made plaster casts of some of the steles, which may be seen in the British Museum now. An American named E. H.

Thompson also read Stephens' book and went to Chichén Itzá. There he became fascinated with the legend of ancient sacrifices at the Sacred Well and nearly lost his life diving into the dark water to recover bones and precious objects that had been thrown there centuries before in sacrificial rites.

Today, with the advantages of modern travel and new archaeological methods, a great many groups of men are working in the Mayan ruins. There are archaeologists sent by the governments of Mexico and Honduras, by the British Museum and the Carnegie Institution of Washington, from the University of Pennsylvania, Harvard, Yale, and other universities.

Every year these new expeditions bring forth new treasures, new proofs of the glory of that greatest ancient American civilization which Mr. Stephens and Mr. Catherwood first explored.

There is a postscript to this story of John Lloyd Stephens. Some time after he had finished his explorations he became interested in the idea of building a canal across the Isthmus of Panama. He was in Panama in 1849 discussing plans, when a German businessman named Heinrich Schliemann, who was later to become famous in the field of archaeology, stopped there on his way to California. The two men met, but there is no record that when they talked together they discussed archaeology at all.

10.

Heinrich Schliemann and the Gold of Troy

Bückow is a little village in the German duchy of Mecklen-
burg-Schwerin, and there in 1822 Heinrich Schliemann was
born. His father was the village pastor and the family was
very poor. But the pastor knew Greek and Latin as well as
his own tongue, so, sitting under the linden tree in the dooryard of their little house, he used to tell the boy the legends
of Greece and Rome. By the time he was seven Heinrich
knew the *Iliad* and the *Odyssey* well. He knew how Paris
carried the beautiful Helen off to Troy, knew how the Greek
kings came to fight for her, knew how Aeneas carried his old

father from burning Troy on his back, and all about Odysseus' wanderings across the "wine-dark sea." The boy believed that every incident in the old stories was exactly true.

After Heinrich Schleimann had grown up, he still believed the old stories. More and more he wanted to go to see the places where these great deeds had been done. But no one could travel unless he was rich, he found out. So Heinrich Schliemann had to earn money.

When he was fourteen he was apprenticed to the owner of a grocery store. There, while he sold the herring, milk, or salt, or ground the potatoes to be distilled for liquor, or swept out the shop and set the shelves in order, he dreamed of the great deeds of the Homeric heroes. He worked thus, dreaming as he worked, for five and a half years. Then in 1841 he had completed his apprenticeship, and he went to Hamburg.

Hamburg is a harbor city and its life was the life of ships and the sea. Soon Schliemann decided to abandon groceries; he embarked as a cabin boy on a ship bound for Venezuela.

But the ship never reached its port. It foundered in a terrible storm in the North Sea, off the coast of Holland. The cabin boy was taken half-conscious from the water and carried to a hospital in Amsterdam. When he left the hospital, he was offered work in an Amsterdam office. The pay was very poor, and the little room which was the only one he could afford was bare and unheated. But he was not unhappy. Through the evenings he was free to study. He wanted to learn languages so that he could use them when he traveled in the countries of which he dreamed so much.

"These exacting and strenuous studies," he wrote later, "within a year had so strengthened my memory that the effort of learning Dutch, Spanish, Italian, and Portuguese seemed very easy. Six weeks spent on any one of these languages, and I could speak and write it fluently."

The neighbors complained because he recited long passages in foreign languages at the top of his voice. He had to move several times because of these complaints, but he persevered.

Meantime the owners of his firm found the boy industrious and clever and put him in charge of foreign correspondence. Soon he wanted to study Russian, for much of the business was with Russia. It is a difficult language, and he could find no Russians in Amsterdam to help him with it. But finally he got hold of an old Russian grammar and a translation of a Russian book called *Telemachus*; with these he went to work.

Not long after that he started in business for himself. At first it was the indigo business, and then during the Crimean War he filled military contracts. He was quickly successful.

Now he went to America — it was the time of the Gold Rush. He was in California when that state joined the Union, so he automatically became an American citizen — a very prosperous American citizen, it may be added.

In all these years, while his fortune was growing larger and larger, Schliemann continued to study. He could speak and write seven or eight languages, and the events in the *Iliad* and *Odyssey* were as vivid to him as ever.

In 1863 he decided to give up business; he had made money enough. He wrote later: "My enterprises had been wonderfully blessed by Heaven to such a degree that by the end of the year 1863 I was already in possession of means far beyond my most ambitious expectations. . . . I now retired from business so that I could devote myself completely to the studies that so fascinated me."

He was forty-one when he decided that he would stop dreaming of those old places his father had described, and go to see them for himself. He would go to the site of ancient Troy; he would find the very stones of Priam's palace walls; he would find the gate through which the Greeks had smuggled their soldiers in the wooden horse; he would see the plain where Hector had fought Achilles. All these things would mean far more to him than any further fortune he could make.

After two years of travel in the East, Schliemann kept his promise to himself. He set about investing his large fortune in the exploration of the site of Troy.

But where exactly could he find ancient Troy? After arriving in Asia Minor, he began to inquire. Tradition said that the ancient town had been situated near the village of Bunarbashi, where a little mound now stood. Schliemann went there, but he was soon convinced that this could not be the place. Not a single potsherd nor a single stone monument had ever been found in this neighborhood. The mound was not big enough to hold such a grand palace as Priam's, and besides all this, it was too far from the sea. According to the *Iliad*, warriors had gone back and forth to their ships several times a day. That would have been impossible here.

There was a much bigger mound near the village of Hissarlik, about 4 miles from the Dardanelles. It was oval in shape and about 3 miles long. Schliemann was sure this was the place where Troy had stood.

As soon as he had procured a good collection of spades, picks, and baskets, and employed some natives to dig for him, he set out for Hissarlik. There he sank a shaft straight down into the middle of the mound — and was rewarded almost at once.

Deeper and deeper he sank the shaft, throwing aside shovelfuls of dirt and with it broken shards and metal objects. Recklessly he rolled aside big stones that had been foundation walls and ripped away crumbling old bricks. He dug down through the mound, destroying as he went. A modern archaeologist, accustomed to examining and photographing every fragment, to investigating not only the precious objects he finds but all their surroundings, would have groaned when he saw Schliemann's work. But no one was there to criticize him, and modern archaeological methods had not yet been invented. So the dirt flew.

Now it became clear to Schliemann that more than one city had been built in this mound; there were indeed several, placed one on top of another. Some of them appeared to show evidence of having been burned. He could not tell what had happened to the others. Was it earthquake? Or war?

Or plague? He could not tell. Their roofs had fallen in; their walls had crumbled; the dust had sifted down on them; and they were gone, each one effaced as if it had never been, before another was placed on top of it.

Wondering about what appeared to be this strange succession of cities, Schliemann dug on. The generations of man at the mound at Hissarlik had certainly come and gone "like to the leaves of the forest." Penetrating the mound, Schliemann later found that nine separate cities had been built at this place. The question he must answer was, Which was Homer's Troy?

At first he thought Troy must be the oldest city, the one at the bottom, so he hacked away through the others, destroying many precious objects. But then he came upon another, the sixth from the top, and this was a burned city grander in its dimensions than the others and so rich in weapons and gold jewelry that he was sure this was what he was looking for.

This city was enclosed by great wall, built of huge stones, with a superstucture of dried brick and with towers and strongly fortified gates. He could trace wide streets between the houses, and the houses were large; sometimes they even had second stories.

Modern archaeologists believe that this sixth city which Schliemann found was not Troy but a city of what they call "middle pre-Mycenaean culture," that it was perhaps a thousand years older than Troy. It is thought now that Troy was actually in the first part of the fourth layer, but Schliemann

of course knew nothing of this. He proclaimed that he had found the old city of the Homeric poems, and all Europe was stirred.

That was 1871. In the two years following, he continued to dig, employing now a hundred workers. There were difficulties enough. The water was bad, and there were clouds of mosquitoes that carried diseases. Sometimes the diggers tried to steal and sell the objects they found. The scholars sitting in their comfortable libraries in various parts of Europe often mocked Schliemann's work. Nevertheless he kept on.

In 1869 he had married a Greek girl named Sophia Engastromenos, and she helped him with the work. By June 1873, they had removed about 350,000 cubic yards of earth from the mound at Hissarlik. June 15 of that year was the date he had set to stop digging.

On June 14 he went with his wife to supervise the digging. This was to be their last day's work. The morning was very hot, and the work was proceeding slowly, when suddenly Schliemann's quick eye saw a glitter near the great stones of the wall of what he called Priam's palace. He drew in his breath sharply. Then, "Tell the men to put down their shovels," he called to the overseer. "We have dug enough. This will be a holiday. I have just remembered, it is my birthday."

After the men had gone, Schliemann and his wife began digging at the base of the wall. "With all possible speed I cut out the treasure with a large knife. I did this by dint of strenuous effort and in frightful danger of losing my life; for the heavy citadel wall which I had to dig under might have crashed down on me at any moment. But the sight of so many priceless objects made me foolhardy and I did not think of the hazards."

There were golden diadems and brooches, chains, and bracelets, all heaped together in a jumbled mass. Someone had apparently packed them hastily and dropped them beside the wall. The box or chest which had held them had disintegrated, but the golden jewels lay gleaming in the dust as they had lain for thousands of years.

Now Heinrich Schliemann and Sophia took the things they found and tied them in the shawl she had been wearing. They carried the bundle secretly to a wooden hut and closed the shutters and lighted a candle, before they took the treasure from the shawl. Then Schliemann picked up a richly carved gold necklace and placed it around his wife's neck, and he hung two golden pendants on her ears. The lovely Greek Helen had worn these things three thousand years before, he thought, but he was sure that she had not been more beautiful than his own Greek wife Sophia as she stood there in the candlelight.

When news of the find leaked out, the Turkish government sent officers to search Schliemann's house, for they claimed that under the law the treasure was Turkish property. They found nothing. With the help of Sophia's relatives, the treasure had been smuggled to Athens.

Certainly Schliemann had no right to send the treasure out of the country. If it had been discovered today the finder would undoubtedly have left it in Turkey or agreed to take a part of it as payment for having found it. But in Schliemann's day ethical practices in archaeology had not been established and no one considered this as robbery.

In 1875 Schliemann asked the Turkish government for a license to resume digging at Hissarlik, but the Turks delayed in granting it. They were bitter about the loss of the treasure he had smuggled out of their country. This hardly mattered to Schliemann, however, for he had begun new excavations at Mycenae, an ancient city near the coast of southern Greece. King Agamemnon, according to the Homeric legend, had left his palace here to go to Troy and bring Helen back again. Legend had it that Mycenae was an even richer city than Troy.

There was some doubt about exactly where Mycenae lay, but a great stone gate carved with two rearing lions stood near some little hillocks that local people said had been bakers' ovens. Schliemann decided that this gate might perhaps have been the entrance to the Mycenaean citadel, that Agamemnon might have led his soldiers through it on his way to Troy. So Schliemann began to dig.

He had not dug deep when he came to a dome-shaped subterranean room. The Greek historian Pausanias had said that King Agamemnon and his followers were buried "in such fashion that the heroes' graves would be in the midst of the meeting place."

At a depth of 26 feet were fragments of pottery, gems, beads, friezes, painted vases, stone molds that might have been used for casting objects of gold and silver. He dug on. Here at last was a grave. He opened it up. Beneath it he cleared away 3 feet of stone and rubble. And then he came on five more graves. A sixth was found later.

The graves were arranged in a great circle and sixteen skeletons were found in them. With them was an immense treasure of gold, silver, bronze, precious stones, and ivory objects. In excitement Schliemann sent a message to the King of Greece:

It is with extraordinary pleasure that I announce to Your Majesty my discovery of the graves which according to tradition are those of Agamemnon, Cassandra, Eurymedon, and their comrades, all killed during the banquet by Clytemnestra and her lover Aegisthus. . . . The bodies were literally covered with gold and jewels.

Modern scholars deny that the skeletons were those of Agamemnon and the others. No one, however, can deny that they were covered with gold and jewels. Schliemann had found a treasure trove richer by far than any found in any land up to that time. "All the museums in the world do not have one-fifth as much," he wrote triumphantly.

In 1882, Schliemann invited William Dörpfeld, a German archaeologist, to help him in his work. Dörpfeld dug systematically so that less was destroyed in the digging. Together the two men undertook to explore the ancient city of Tiryns, which also was situated in southern Greece not far from Mycenae. Here they uncovered rock foundations which gave the complete ground plan of a sumptuous palace, a palace grander in its proportions than any structure they had ever looked on. From Tiryns, they knew from the old poems, the heroes had set out across the sea to fight in the Trojan War.

The old ruins inside the mounds at Hissarlik, Mycenae, and now Tiryns — certainly the past of the old Aegean peoples was coming alive again as the industrious spades shoveled the dirt from the stones. Throughout Europe, as the news of his work spread, Schliemann was becoming a personage, admired and acclaimed and treated with honor. And still he continued to dig; and his enthusiasm did not lessen. "It is an entirely new and unsuspected world that I am discovering for archaeology," he wrote proudly.

At the dead city of Tiryns Schliemann had found vases and jars with geometric patterns like those found on the Aegean Islands and especially on the island of Crete. He wanted to prove that he had discovered a culture which had spread across the whole east coast of Greece even earlier than Homeric times. "I should like to crown my career with one great piece of work," he wrote, "namely with the excavation of the extremely old prehistoric palace at Knossus on Crete which I believe I discovered three years ago. . . ."

But perhaps Schliemann had done enough for one lifetime. He was not to uncover the great civilization which scholars now call Minoan-Mycenaean. He died suddenly at Naples on Christmas Day, 1890.

Some time before his death he had the golden treasure that he had unearthed crated and sent to Berlin. There at a royal reception it was handed over "to the German nation in perpetual possession and inalienable custody." Crown Prince Wilhelm, who was later to be Kaiser Wilhelm II, escorted Sophia to the banquet.

Now the treasure was housed in a wing of the Völkerkundemuseum for all to see, and Schliemann's name was written in golden letters over the door. There it was to stay until the time of the Second World War. Then it was removed and put in a secret bunker of the Berlin Zoo for safekeeping. But when the Russian troops entered Berlin in the spring of 1945 they found the treasure and sent it back through the lines. Schliemann's gold of "Troy" and of Mycenae must be somewhere in Russia today.

II.

A King Crowned with Flowers

After Schliemann had made his finds at Mycenae and Tiryns, European scholars became more and more sure that a great maritime people must have lived along the shores of the Mediterranean Sea, perhaps a thousand years before the Greeks arrived there. Greek history and legend seemed to confirm this idea.

An early Greek historian stated that "The first person known to us as having established a navy is Minos. He made himself master of what is now called the Hellenic Sea and ruled over the Cyclades, into most of which he sent the first colonies. . . ."

119

This King Minos was well known in Greek legend. According to the myths he had a splendid palace on the island of Crete and under his palace he had built a labyrinth where the Minotaur was kept. There the brave Theseus fought and killed that fabled beast, and Ariadne guided him to safety with a silken thread.

Tradition pointed to Minos as a great and powerful king, and to Knossos as the center of a widespread empire, but tradition is an unsubstantial thing. There were no facts to prove that the Minoans ever existed, or that King Minos ever lived. The island of Crete was beautiful, with snow-capped mountains and level plains, with olive trees and flocks of black goats, and with carefree peasants who lived in humble cottages. And that was all — all that is, unless you counted some big gypsum blocks covered with a strange kind of writing that stood on a hill called "Gentleman's Head" overlooking the sea. No one paid any attention to them.

No one paid any attention to the big gypsum blocks with their queer inscriptions until the Englishman Arthur Evans came to Crete at the end of the nineteenth century.

Arthur Evans, a rich and cultured gentleman who was curator of the Ashmolean Museum at Oxford, was an authority on Greek coins, and a collector of seal stones. He was in fact looking for seal stones that summer day he landed in Crete. He was not particularly interested in archaeology, but he was fascinated when he saw the tall blocks with their inscriptions at Gentleman's Head. Soon he was wondering how they came to be there, and whether anything lay in the hill beneath them. He decided that he would buy the property and begin excavating.

So it was not long before the picks and shovels were at work, and Evans kept on digging for a quarter of a century.

The buildings he uncovered were only a few feet below the ground, but he dug with meticulous care. There was no reckless destruction here like that of Schliemann at the site of Troy. And the building Evans found beneath the grassy earth was a staggering thing — the greatest ancient structure that archaeologists have ever found. It covered six acres: the palace of a mighty king.

The outer walls of the palace were made of slabs of dressed stone, still in good condition. There was only one entrance, and this faced the north, as if the builders might have feared attack from sea raiders. The palace rooms were curiously arranged, for they were set at varying levels, so that the roof of one room served as a terrace for the one behind it. Light came into these rooms through windows that opened on shafts or long porticoes. Here and there Evans found open courtyards paved with flagstones and cement, while wide flights of stairs led from one level to the next.

The roofs of the inside rooms had been supported on wooden columns that tapered down to their stone bases. The columns had rotted away, but their form could still be detected in the surrounding earth.

Digging with the utmost caution and precision so that as little as possible might be destroyed, Evans now uncovered

one room after another. Some were well preserved, others
had crumbled walls and fallen ceilings. He found a throne
room, the high-backed stone throne still in place, the walls
surrounded with low benches where the courtiers once had
sat. He found a great courtyard, 300 feet long, where state
ceremonials had been held; he found twenty-two storerooms
where jars, each taller than a man, stood in neat rows. These
jars once had held oil, grain, and wine. And below the palace
storerooms were found the palace kitchens.

The royal living apartments were sunk deep into the side
of the hill, well protected. Evans penetrated them with great
curiosity. A bathroom was here with cemented floor and oval
earthenware tub. Rain water for the tub was carried by
spouts from roofs, courts, and terraces and led downhill in
cleverly designed terra-cotta pipes.

Beds, chairs, and tables in the royal chambers were still in
place, and in one of them was a shrine with a terra-cotta
image of a goddess surrounded by doves. Vessels for offerings
and sacred horns, which held double axes, symbolic of sacrifice, stood beside the shrine.

There were two large stone chests in one of these rooms.
Evans raised the lid of one of them and lifted from it the
image of a little snake goddess. She was made of terra cotta
glazed with bright colors. The proud little lady stood erect,
her head thrown back and her arms extended, and in each
hand she held a golden serpent which coiled about her arms
up to the elbow. Curiously Evans examined her costume.
She wore a tall tiara perched on her elaborately curled hair,

and around the tiara, and also her waist, were coiled snakes. Her dress had a tight-fitted bodice and a long flounced skirt that extended to her ankles. There was something startlingly modern about the little figure that had lain in the dark of the chest through so many thousands of years.

All the time that Evans and his aides were uncovering the wide staircases, he had wondered what the people looked like who had created these things. Then one day he came upon a life-sized portrait of one of them on a wall of the palace. The figure was that of the cupbearer of King Minos' court. The youth was unshaven, with curly hair and reddish skin. Graceful and erect, he seemed to lean backward a little as he carried a tall, elaborately carved gold cup. His profile looked very much like that of an ancient Greek, and Evans noticed that he had an exceedingly small waist. He guessed later, after he had seen more Cretan paintings, that small waists were the fashion among the young men of that day.

Evans was congratulating himself on the fact that the appearance of King Minos' courtiers was no longer unknown to him, when he discovered another wall portrait which he believed was of Minos himself. The King was not arrayed in royal robes, nor did he have a crown or a scepter. He was not shown, like many other monarchs, hunting wild beasts or vanquishing his enemies. He was young and graceful, and he was walking in a field of crocuses, leaning down as if to gather them. The colors of that painting were so fresh and delicate that the flowers seemed to glow in the pale sunlight that penetrated the palace chamber. The youth wore a necklet of lilies and there was a crown of lilies on his head. From that crown three peacock feathers swept gracefully back. Evans, looking at him, felt that this youth possessed something more than kingly power, that he was "the representative on earth of the Minoan Mother Goddess." The master of the Cretan palace was not only a king, but a god.

Gradually the palace chambers seemed to Evans no longer deserted, for in one part he found paintings on almost every wall. They seemed to live and sparkle, to bubble with joyousness. Here was a cat stalking pheasants, here a bluebird, and here a Sudanese monkey. In one room there was a frieze of dolphins and flying fish that played over rippling waves, and in others there were plants drawn with such splendidly free and curving lines that you could almost think the wind was blowing them.

Plants, animals, and fish, however, were not the only wall designs. There were people — boys and girls jumping over the backs of bulls, people in grand processions, people in crowds. Arthur Evans, writing a report on the paintings, paused to speculate on these people:

Sometimes the dependents of the prince march into the palace in stately procession, bringing gifts. Sometimes the court is filled with gaily adorned dames and curled gentlemen, standing, sitting, gesticulating vigorously and flirting. We see the ladies, like Oriental women, trying to preserve the fresh whiteness of their complexion. Again the people of the court are watching a troop of bull trainers.

The people of the court were accustomed to fine clothing, Evans thought, to jewelry and beautiful furniture. They had vases that were lovely in form and finish, porcelain cups of eggshell thinness, engraved gems and dagger blades inlaid with gold. Once he found a chess board that blazed with gold and silver, with ivory and crystal.

Evans beheld all these things, but still he did not know who the people were who had made and used them. Judging by the grandeur of the palace, he knew that they were rich and gifted, traders probably whose ships plied the waters of the Eastern Mediterranean and who did business in the ports of Asia Minor and of Egypt. Probably their cargoes were of grain, wine, and oil. But beyond this Evans knew nothing as he continued to uncover room after room of the great palace and its neighboring buildings.

Now he began to wonder what to do with the mounting list of objects he found. The Greek government objected to their being taken out of the country and required that they be placed in a specially built museum in the nearby town of Candia. Here, therefore, Evans placed the weapons, pottery, seal stones, and illegible engraved tablets, after all these had been chemically treated to preserve them. Here also the frescoes, painstakingly taken down from the palace walls, were put on display.

The museum was a commodious one and the objects were well displayed, but it was not proof against earthquakes. Twice it has been shaken with earth tremors, and its ceilings have fallen with some damage to the objects on display. It

is fortunate that copies of a good many of the objects have
been placed in other museums.

Arthur Evans worried a good deal lest the precious Minoan
objects might be hurt, and he felt too that when they were
displayed in museum cases they appeared lifeless and dull.
They seemed somehow to have very little connection with
the men who had made and used them. He wanted people
to understand how beautiful the great palace at Knossos had
been. And he decided finally that he would use the fortune
that he had inherited from his father, to restore the palace
of Minos. He could not bring the people back to it, but he
could try to make it as it was when they had lived here. He
could replace the rotted wooden beams and pillars with
steel girders, he could rebuild the walls that had crumbled,
he could have the bright frescoes copied and put the copies
into the rooms where the originals had been. Modern engineering would make the structure safe from earthquake now.

So he started to build, and soon on the hill that looked out
over the flowery pastures, the vineyards, and the olive groves,
the structure that had been a confused mass of rubble took
form again. He wrote in his report:

It is indeed rarely that natural conditions allow an ancient
building of three or four stories to be dug out, its charred beams
carefully replaced with iron girders, and its calcined pillars replaced by new, on the old lines, so that we can mount, as at
Knossos, an ancient grand stairway of three flights on its original
steps above us as we mount, in their proper place, as they were
built.

In this way Evans spent a fortune in unearthing and restor-
ing the great palace of Minos and in making it proof against
earthquake shocks. But he knew very little of what had
transpired there in ancient times. He seemed to have proof
that the palace had been built, destroyed, and rebuilt at
three different times, and he was able to tell by comparing
the artifacts he found with similar Egyptian objects which
were datable, that the first walls had been raised as early
as 3400 B.C. but that the building had not been finished until
about 1400 B.C. But who were the people who had lived
there so joyously? What had become of them? He could not
tell. Had they been driven off by sea raiders? Or did they
die of some dreadful plague? Had the walls and pillars of
those bright rooms been tumbled together by earthquakes?
There was no way of knowing.

Evans died in 1941, and the mystery was still unsolved.
He had been sure that if he could only decipher the Cretan
writing he could find out what had happened at Knossos,
and he worked secretly, not wanting to depend on the help
of others. He was able to distinguish three different kinds
of Cretan writing. First, there were the little marks on the
seal stones which had interested him before he left London.
These were tiny stars, arrows, heads, hands, and other figures. He found the same marks on lumps of clay which
turned up here and there on the island. He called them
hieroglyphics and judged that they were very old, that they
had probably been made some time between 1700 and 1500
B.C.

But these were not all. In various places he found inscriptions written in what seemed to be mere outlines of the hieroglyphic figures. He called this writing "Linear A." About 150 tablets written in this Linear A were uncovered at the site of a Cretan palace a few miles from the town of Phaistos not far from Knossos.

Now, as he studied this Linear A and puzzled over the hidden meaning of its characters, he found some tablets written in a different script. At some time Linear A apparently had been modified gradually and then replaced altogether by this new kind of writing, which he called "Linear B."

Great numbers of inscribed tablets had been unearthed at the palace of Knossos, and on examination they turned out to be written in Linear B. Evans found that there were between three and four thousand. The great palace had been destroyed by fire in the fifteenth century B.C., and Linear B was apparently in use at that time.

That was all Evans could find out. But meantime other archaeologists were working along the shores of Greece. In 1939 at Pylos, which is on the western side of Peloponnesus, Carl Blegen, an American archaeologist, found six hundred clay tablets inscribed in Linear B. What was this Cretan writing doing on the shores of Greece? What had the connection between Knossos and Pylos been? Had the two peoples simply traded with each other and so learned each other's ways? Or had the Cretans ruled over a great maritime empire that included the shores of Greece, as Evans had believed? It was possible, however, that the dwellers along the Aegean shore had been the Cretans' enemies, that they had sailed to Knossos, and that their men had sacked and burned the great palace that looked out over the sea.

It was not until ten years after Evans' death that Linear B was read. It was deciphered by an Englishman, Michael Ventris. Ventris, who was an architect by profession, had been a bomber navigator in World War II, and all his life he had been fascinated with languages. He succeeded in solving the mystery of Linear B by using the method the army used for breaking codes, and he came to the conclusion that this language was really Greek.

In June 1952 Ventris gave a radio address for the British Broadcasting Company and he said: "During the last few weeks I have come to the conclusion that the Knossos and Pylos tablets must after all be written in Greek — a difficult and archaic Greek, seeing that it is five hundred years older than Homer and written in a rather abbreviated form, but Greek, nevertheless."

Ventris published a book describing his great discovery in 1956. Later that year he was killed in an automobile accident. He was only thirty-four years old.

But Ventris' work had given a new stimulus to the work of the archaeologists in Greece, and many more tablets inscribed in Linear B were now turned up, not only at Pylos but in other places. There was plenty of material for scholars to work on.

Almost all the tablets they studied were inventories. Ventris had deciphered one such inventory — a list of wine jars and cups, some with two handles, some with four, some broken, and so on. Now a great many other tablets were read. There were lists of slaves, of sewing women, of soldiers and carpenters, of ship builders and potters. From those lists it was possible to rediscover many of the men and women who had lived and worked in the old Aegean cities and in Crete fifteen hundred years before Christ was born.

But inventories and lists must surely comprise only a part of a people's life. Were there no poems? No letters? No chronicles of great deeds, or legends, or history of the reigns of kings? No tablets with records such as this have yet been found.

And while some scholars work eagerly to read in the Linear B tablets of the life of a people who perished more than five hundred years before Homer's time, others are working at the decipherment of Linear A. They have not yet succeeded.

Meantime, while all the tablets have not yet been read, more will certainly be found. Some day a tablet may come to light that tells what happened to that mighty Cretan palace that looked out across the sea so many centuries ago.

Part II
The Search for Understanding

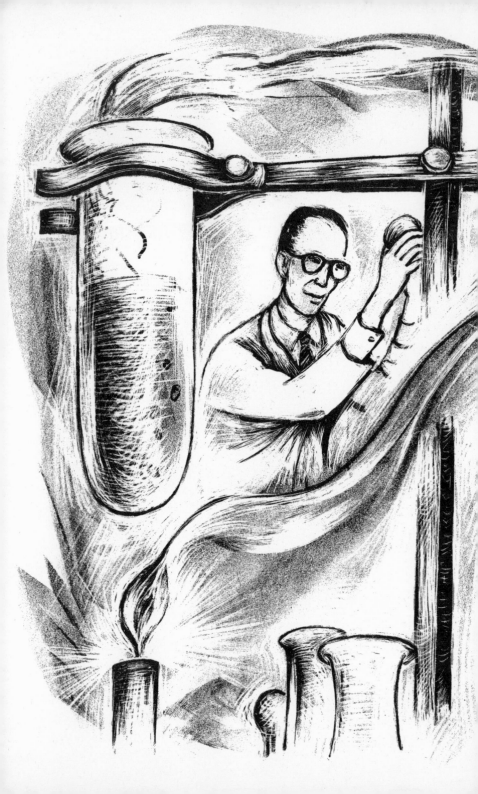

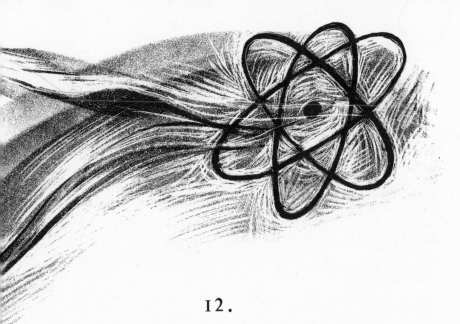

12.

Romance Changes to Scientific Inquiry

For a hundred years and more archaeology was romance —
the romance of unexpected beauty and strangeness, the discovery of what men only dimly knew had once existed. But
gradually, as the spirit of the age changed, the attitude of
the archaeologists changed too. It was no longer enough to
admire the treasures that had been hidden in ancient tombs
or covered by deposits of clay or silt; the world was growing scientific and the ways of the archaeologists were becoming scientific, as well.

This new scientific spirit was seen in the precise and careful methods which archaeologists gradually developed. There
was no hasty destruction of surroundings now as gold and
jewels and other treasures were unearthed. Each stratum of

earth was carefully cut through, every smallest man-made fragment collected and labeled, every discovery recorded, every object chemically treated lest it disintegrate when exposed to the air or light.

Neither was there any jumping to conclusions now. Botta's announcement that Nineveh had been found would never have been sent if he had shared today's scientific spirit; Heinrich Schliemann would not have been able to claim that he had found Troy.

One question these new scientific archaeologists sought continually to answer was the question of the age of the objects they unearthed. They wanted to find some method of dating them and of piecing together the dates into the long, continuous story of man's life on earth.

For long the world had depended on history for an understanding of the past, and it was said that history began when men first learned to write. But writing was not invented until about five thousand years ago, and men had been living on earth for long, long ages before that. Ancient tools and weapons, even whole cities upon whose makers history sheds no light, have been dug from the earth or raised from the sea. The historian needs the archaeologist to complement his work.

It was not very hard to reconstruct the past of Egypt, whose history is older than that of any other in the Western world, for the Egyptians learned to write very early and left many inscriptions on the walls of their temples and tombs. So complete were these records that Flinders Petrie and others were able to make a long list of the Pharaohs with the length of each one's reign.

But Egypt is only one country, and there are countless places where it is impossible to make a consecutive list of monarchs. In some of these places the material on which records were kept was perishable; in others no known records were kept at all. So if the name of some great king survived in legend, no one could tell exactly when he lived.

When exactly did Hammurabi reign? Scholars had picked out no fewer than four different dates for him, and it was possible that none of them was right. When was the great city of Zimbabwe in southern Rhodesia built? When did men first come to the Americas? When were the tall stone pillars set up in their curious pattern at Stonehenge? Until recently no one knew any of these things.

In the last half of the nineteenth century Oskar Montelius of Sweden, observing that fashions knew no boundaries, studied and compared the designs with which weapons and jewelry were decorated in an effort to find out when they were made. A brooch made in Crete might be ornamented in the same way as another made in Egypt, and if the Egyptian brooch was found in the tomb of a Pharaoh whose date was known, then probably the Cretan piece that bore the same design was made about the same time. In a general way the time of the Cretan owner could be guessed at. But the comparison of designs was a tedious and rather unreliable way of working; soon other men were trying different methods.

One of these was Baron Gerard de Geer, the Swedish geologist. De Geer knew that most of Europe and America had once been covered by great sheets of ice and that when the ice retreated at the end of the fourth and last glacial period, it left clayey deposits along the Baltic coasts of Sweden and Finland. In successive winters the layers of fine black clay had been laid down under the ice cap, and in the summers when the ice receded, the melting water deposited light sand of coarser grain. The alternate dark and light layers deposited year by year were called "varves." De Geer found it was possible to count the years by counting the varves. He could reckon the age of a flint arrowhead or a stone ax by the layer in which it had been embedded. In this way time could be measured only in places that had been covered by the ice sheet, and, of course, much of the world did not lie within this area.

While neither the comparison of designs nor the counting of varves was very satisfactory, they were a beginning. Then a good many other methods were brought forward. It was found that the age of various strata of earth could be estimated by the fossil bones of animals that had been destroyed by the changes in climate that accompanied the movements of glaciers. This discovery opened up all sorts of possibilities. Such fossils proved that the dry wastes of the Sahara Desert had once been lush and green, for the bones of hippopotamuses and crocodiles were found there, and that the Central United States had once been tropical, for the bones of elephants were found on what is now the Western Plains.

As the archaeologists searched further they found that some approximation of accuracy in dating might be had by counting tree rings, for the growth of a tree reveals itself when its trunk is cut through horizontally. The horizontal section bears concentric rings, each one of which represents the tree's growth for one year. In spring the growth cells are larger and light-colored; in summer they are smaller and darker. Since there is a direct relation between the thickness of the tree rings and the intensity of the sun's radiation, all the trees of a particular region must grow at the same rate, and it is possible to chart the passing years by charting the rings. In this way it is possible to fix the age of ancient timber.

Of course, dating by tree rings can be done only where people have been accustomed to building with wood. But the method has been successfully used in California for dating some buildings made by the pre-Columbian Indians, and archaeologists hope in this way to find out the age of some beautiful wood carvings that have been found in the Congo.

Counting growth rings is not the only way in which the archaeologist has been able to use trees for dating. There is also a method of learning the passage of time by tree pollen. Pollen is so hard that it is practically indestructible. A sample of pollen found in a peat bog will show what kind of forest covered the land at the time the peat was laid down and therefore how old it is. For the forests have always succeeded one another in a regular order — first the birch forest, then the pine forest, then the oak, and finally the beech. So if the pollen comes from an oak tree, then the peat where it was found was made when an oak forest covered the land, or if the pollen is of a birch tree, then the peat is much older. Any object found in the peat-bed bearing tree pollen may therefore be dated chronologically in a rough way.

All these methods of dating were ingenious but none of them were really very satisfactory, and many ancient objects continued to hide the secret of their age. Only in our own time did Willard Libby find a way to make them give up their secrets: it was he who worked out the radiocarbon method of dating.

Willard Libby was a nuclear physicist from the University of California. For four years during World War II, he worked on the Manhattan Project, which developed the first atomic bomb. In the course of this work he became interested in radioactive carbon.

Carbon is one of the basic substances of which all animal and plant matter is composed. In the form of carbon dioxide it is an important part of the earth's atmosphere. Most of the carbon atoms in the molecules of this carbon dioxide are ordinary carbon, which has an atomic weight of 12. But a very small amount consists of a heavier radioactive form called radiocarbon, with an atomic weight of 14, which is being continuously produced in the upper atmosphere by cosmic rays.

As plants absorb carbon dioxide from the air and use it in the production of their food, carbon-14 is incorporated into the plant tissues. Animals, by eating plants or other animals that have eaten plants, ingest the carbon-14 atoms, which in turn become part of the animal tissues.

As long as the plant or animal lives, it continues to absorb radiocarbon and to maintain a constant amount of it in its tissues. When the organism dies, however, all metabolic processes cease and there is no new supply of carbon-14. Then the amount of radiocarbon gradually diminishes at a rate determined by the radioactive decay of carbon-14.

By 1946 Libby reasoned that measuring the amount of radiocarbon left in ancient organic remains would give an accurate way of determining when the organisms had died.

Research proved that half the radiocarbon in any substance reverts to ordinary carbon in the space of about fifty-six hundred years. After another fifty-six hundred years only a quarter of the original is left; at the end of a third period the radiocarbon is reduced to an eighth, and so on, until after about forty thousand years, too little is left to be detected with any degree of accuracy. So with a Geiger counter Libby could calculate the age of a piece of wood or bone or other organic matter less than forty thousand years old by measuring the amount of radioactive carbon it contained.

Of course it was not really so simple as that. If dating by the radiocarbon method was to be reliable, it was necessary to select and prepare each sample with the utmost care. The purified sample must be reduced to carbon dioxide and then to pure carbon, and this requires intricate chemical steps to be taken before reasonable accuracy may be expected from the Geiger-counter readings.

With infinite precision Willard Libby had worked out his instruments; now it remained only to test them. Looking at his complicated maze of tubes, valves, and flasks, he knew that pieces of old wood or bone or charcoal taken from the sites of ancient campfires would reveal their age to him.

In 1948 four archaeologists from the American Anthropological Association agreed to help him. They brought samples of ancient objects for him to try. At first he asked them to bring only samples that could be dated in other ways: objects from temples of known Egyptian Pharaohs, or from Roman encampments of known date. Each time he put the sample into his apparatus and awaited the result. Sometimes he waited a thousand minutes, occasionally as much as two days and nights. Then when the Geiger counter had ticked off its result he compared it with the known date. Each time the Geiger counter's reckoning was within a small percentage of the known dates.

So radiocarbon dating had proved itself, and Libby began to try samples of bone, wood, and charcoal of unknown date. Archaeologists everywhere were now eager to submit their specimens to him. Small packages mailed from all over the world came streaming into his laboratory. One writer has said that the archaeologists now were collecting flecks of charcoal as carefully "as if the Queen of England had dropped her pearl necklace into the gutter."

There are now a score of laboratories where radiocarbon dating is done. The first one outside the United States was in Cambridge, England, the next in Copenhagen, Denmark.

With experimentation by many minds the apparatus has now become more refined and sensitive. At first it was necessary to have several ounces of carbon for testing, but as the process was perfected as little as 1/100 of an ounce could be used. More sensitive apparatus made it possible to detect the radioactivity in a tiny sample that is forty thousand years old, the limit for radiocarbon dating.

By Willard Libby's method many hitherto unanswered questions have been solved. We know now, for example, that Zimbabwe was not built until 575 A.D., and that Hammurabi came to his throne about 1750 B.C. And we can assign a date for the erection of Stonehenge, whose giant menhirs in England have puzzled beholders so long. Dozens of baffling questions are now being answered as the dates come popping from the Geiger counters, and new estimates of age are made, new sequences in time. In 1960 the Nobel Prize was awarded to Willard Libby for his great discovery.

Yet even carbon-14 dating cannot give us all we need to know about dating the past. The radiocarbon method can provide dates back to about forty thousand years — but what about objects that are older than that? And what about inorganic objects, such as stone or bronze artifacts? Scientists are working now on a new method, the potassium-argon technique, that promises to provide accurate measurements of the age of rocks bearing fossils and artifacts much too old for the use of the carbon-14 method. And the archaeologists are searching farther and farther back in time.

13.

The Strange Geometry of Stonehenge

In 1918 Sir Cecil Chubb of Salisbury made a unique gift to the English government. The gift was Stonehenge, a group of rough-hewn stones that stand on the chalk downs of Salisbury Plain. When he presented them to England, Sir Cecil did not know exactly what he was giving. He did not know how these stones came to be in the middle of the plain, or who had dragged them there, or why they were arranged as they were. The only thing he knew was that they had stood there since time immemorial.

The huge cluster of upright stones which he had given his country stands in the center of a level circular space 300 feet wide, surrounded by a ditch and an earthwork. A grassy

road which is now called "the Avenue" enters this space from
the northeast and a single rough boulder called the "Hele
Stone" stands in the center of this road.

Within the outer circle the stones are carefully arranged
in four series. First there is a circle of enormous "sarsen"
stones, some of them 13 feet tall and weighing more than 40
tons. (The word "sarsen" which comes from "Saracen,"
meant anything heathenish to the people of the Middle Ages.
None but the devil himself could have moved them, it was
said.) Originally the sarsens in this great circle were joined
by a line of lintels fastened with crude stone tenons and mor-
tises.

With the passing of time, winds and storms have blown
down the lintels. Some of them still lie on the ground. The
stones of the circle inside the first are somewhat smaller and
of a different kind. They are "bluestones."

Inside the bluestone circle there are sarsen stones again,
and here they are arranged in a big horseshoe. The stones
of the horseshoe have been put up in pairs, each pair topped
by a stone lintel. Each group forms a trilithon.

The trilithons are graduated in size; the tallest one, which
stands opposite the opening of the horseshoe, is more than
22 feet high, with a lintel 16 feet long and 4 feet thick. Only
two trilithons are standing today; originally there were probably eleven.

Finally, inside the horseshoe there are more bluestones,
but only a few of them. Enough remain, however, to show
that they were once arranged in an oval pattern.

At the heart of it all is a great recumbent stone which generations of men have called the "Altar Stone." But whether or not it was an altar, or for what god it was made, no one can say.

What did it mean, this gigantic exercise in geometry, these circles within circles, this colossal horseshoe? Who came here in the days when the patterns of these rocks were understood? What did they do here? Once a wide road led across the down to this place, a highway broad enough for glittering processions — but processions of whom? Were they soldiers? Or priests? Unused as the ages passed, the highway nearly disappeared, obliterated by the encroaching grass. Only very recently were the vague outlines of the road found again by the penetrating eye of a camera carried in an airplane.

Rough, colossal, inscrutable, the strange geometric pattern kept its secrets through the passing centuries. Legends about it have abounded. Some said the wizard Merlin got the devil to whisk these stones from Ireland in a single night. Others said that Queen Boadicea was buried here. A brave and beautiful British woman, she died leading her people in a revolt against the Roman legions. But there was nothing to prove that this was her monument.

Again it was said that this was a monument for Hengist and Horsa, who had come from Jutland to help fight off the Picts and Scots and had stayed to conquer the country for themselves. But nothing remains to show that Hengist and Horsa were buried there, either.

King James I in the seventeenth century apparently wanted to have done with legends. He sent his architect Inigo Jones to examine Stonehenge. Inigo Jones announced that without any doubt it was a Roman temple.

But the theory of Roman origin for the structure did not content the patriotic English. Charles II asked John Aubrey, a noted antiquarian, to investigate further. Aubrey lived not far from Stonehenge in Avebury, where there was another large circle of standing stones. It was generally believed that those stones marked the meeting place of the Druids, the mysterious bards and priests who had been such a powerful influence in England at the time of the Roman occupation. Stonehenge was built by the Druids too, Aubrey announced.

The more he investigated, the more Aubrey was sure the Druids had built Stonehenge. The Roman writers with whose work he was familiar had described the Druid ceremonies; it was said the Druids were accustomed to performing human sacrifices. Did they slaughter their victims here on the Altar Stone? Examining the earth inside the great circle enclosed by the ditch and earthwork, Aubrey found a series of depressions in the ground. Undoubtedly these had been deeper holes which time had filled with silt and earth. Had the Druids once burned the bodies of their victims in these holes? The "Aubrey Holes" fired the imagination of all who came to Stonehenge now, and seemed to make it more certain that Stonehenge had been built by the Druids.

William Stukely, Secretary of the Society of Antiquaries

in 1718, was as sure as anyone else that the Druids had built Stonehenge. He was a doctor of medicine but he was also a minister of the Christian Church, and he was greatly interested in trying to reconcile the Druids' beliefs with the Christians'. Perhaps the Druids had not been so savage, after all, he said; the only accounts of them were those written by the Romans who wanted to eradicate them. Stukely considered the Druids poets and moral teachers, and he rehearsed all the traditions that made the oak tree and the mistletoe sacred to them. There was no doubt in his mind that they had constructed Stonehenge, as he went methodically making the first survey of the place.

Now no one thought of any other origin for Stonehenge, and when in the eighteenth century people became interested in the esoteric widom of the East, it was maintained that the Druids were astrologers and that Stonehenge was a stellar observatory. But there was no more to prove this than that it had been Boadicea's tomb.

The years passed and Stonehenge continued to hold a fascination for antiquarians, who tried again and again to understand it. In the nineteenth century a "Mr. Cunnington" made a great effort but had no success. Sure that he would not be the last one to seek an explanation for the great stones, he hid a bottle of good port wine under the Altar Stone for the refreshment of those who came after. It was not found again till 1920. And all this time people were more and more sure that Stonehenge had been built by the Druids.

Archaeological methods took a great step forward in the twentieth century, and various sciences were now joined together in investigation. Astronomy was one of these.

For some time it had been observed that if you stood behind the Altar Stone at dawn on Midsummer Day and looked straight through the great horseshoe and along the Avenue you would see the sun come up behind the Hele Stone. Scholars believed this orientation proved that the great design must have been made by sun worshipers. Sir Norman Lockyer, the British Royal Astronomer, was much interested in this. It was known that with the slightly irregular movement of the earth the exact point at which the sun rises on a given date each year varies slightly, and by precise calculations it is possible to determine exactly how much. If Stonehenge was oriented to the rising sun on Midsummer Day, it would be possible to find out by astronomical calculations in what year it was built.

In 1901 Sir Norman made these astronomical calculations. Stonehenge was built at a date "lying between 1900 and 1500 B.C.," he announced. But that was a thousand years before anyone ever mentioned Druids in England. If Sir Norman's conclusions were right, the whole fabric of the belief in the Druid construction of Stonehenge was destroyed. And those who looked up at the mammoth stones were more than ever at a loss to understand them.

Astronomy was not the only tool that was used to banish the idea that the Druids had built Stonehenge. While Sir Norman was working out the year in which the sun first rose over the Altar Stone, an archaeologist named Gowland began to excavate. He dug carefully at six different points so that he could compare the things he found at one place with those he found at another. As he dug he noted the exact depth of every man-made object that he found. In all six places there were coins in the first ten-inch layer — a penny of George III, a half-penny of George I, a pewter farthing of James II — and below these were coins of Roman date.

Now Gowland dug deeper. Two or three feet down he found tools of flint, then axes and hammerstones of sandstone, and finally massive pounding hammers, or mauls — the tools that had pounded the great menhirs of Stonehenge into shape. But these were not all. At last, near one of the trilithons, he found a chip of sarsen stone with a small green stain of oxidized copper. This artifact indicated that the builders had lived in the Bronze Age.

Astronomy and archaeology had now confirmed each other. Stonehenge had not been built by the Druids, but a thousand years before their time. In 1950 this date was established in a third way, for charcoal dug from one of the Aubrey Holes confirmed it. Carbon-14 dating placed the construction at 1847 B.C., with a possible variation of 225 years.

So the cool, precise work of the scientists put an end to legends and superstitions. There could be no more talk of Druids at Stonehenge now. Nevertheless, the ancient structure was as mysterious as it had ever been. Whence had the great stones come? Why were they of two different kinds?

Geology was another science that helped find an answer

to these questions. Geological study now proved that the sarsen stones of gray sandstone must have been brought from the Marlborough Downs 24 miles away. But the bluestones were another matter. The nearest place that bluestone was to be found was in the Prescelly mountains in South Wales, 150 miles from Stonehenge. Why these stones were chosen, and how they were transported over the hills and valleys and across the rivers, no one has been able to say.

Stuart Piggott, an eminent British archaeologist, is working at Stonehenge now. He started to excavate in 1950, carefully leaving more than half the area untouched, for he held that the diggers of the future would undoubtedly develop techniques superior to his own and he did not want to spoil their work.

After working some time Piggott announced that the earthworks and big stone circles and the horseshoe were not all put up at the same time. Successive groups came and went, he held, building and destroying and building up again over a period of about four hundred years. He thought the ditch and earthwork, the circle of Aubrey Holes, the Avenue, and the Hele Stone were all part of the original construction built about 1847 B.C. Another group of people made the two rings of bluestones, and later the huge sarsen circle and the trilithon horseshoe were put up. These were the last to be built, and they were made about 1500 B.C.

In all three phases the line between the center of the Altar Stone and the center of the Hele Stone was preserved, proving that all the builders had been sun worshipers and that this was not a monument or a meeting place, but a temple to the sun.

Up to 1953 no more could be found out about Stonehenge and its builders, even with the most modern scientific re-seearch. And then, by accident, a new discovery was made. It was late on a June afternoon, and the sun's rays were striking the surface of one of the sarsens obliquely. They cast small shadows wherever there were scratches or indentations on the stone's surface. One of the excavators noticed what seemed to be a pattern scratched on the stone. He looked more closely and observed that two images had been cut there. One was that of an ax. Its form was familiar enough, for many axes of this type had been uncovered in digging around the sarsens. But the other image was startling. For there, neatly etched, was a dagger — a dagger with a round handle and a long pointed blade. The English had never used daggers of this kind. This was the sort of weapon carried by the Mycenaean Greeks who influenced the culture of the Eastern Mediterranean at the time of the Trojan war. This finding seemed to indicate that the builders of Stonehenge had gone to the Eastern Mediterranean to employ an architect. Here, carved on the stone, was his symbol.

With the finding of the dagger other facts that had been casually observed became significant. There was, for instance, the shape of the sarsens; they bulged slightly, just as the pillars of the Greek temples did. And there was the technique of shaping the stone blocks. They had been banged with the heavy stone mauls which had been found in the ground near them. The granite obelisks of Egypt had been fashioned in exactly the same way.

Was it an architect from the Eastern Mediterranean who was commissioned to design Stonehenge? Did the fame of the Mycenaean Greek builders extend all the way to Britain thirty-five hundred years ago? Was their reputation so great the Britons wanted a "foreigner" to design their precious temple to the sun? The sun itself, striking the stone with the slanting rays of the late afternoon, had posed new questions.

14.

The Mystery of the Scrolls

On a bleak hillside in the wilderness of Judea in February 1947, a Bedouin boy named Muhammed adh-Dhib went searching for a stray goat. The place was about 1¼ miles from the Dead Sea. After a while he came to the entrance of a small cave in the rocks, and, thinking that the goat might be there, he threw in a stone to drive it out. To his surprise he heard a crash of broken pottery.

Next day Muhammed adh-Dhib went to the cave again, this time with a companion. Inside they found the shattered fragments of a pottery jar and several other jars still intact. Each one was about 2 feet tall and about 10 inches in diameter. Lifting the lid of one of them and peering inside they found a dilapidated scroll wrapped in partly disintegrated linen cloth. The Bedouin boys took the scrolls to a merchant in Bethlehem, who mentioned them to another merchant who lived not far away in Jerusalem. In the heart of that Old City the Archbishop Athanasius Yeshue Samuel presided over the little Syrian Orthodox Monastery of St. Mark, which was known to have a fine collection of Syrian manuscripts. The merchants brought the scrolls the Bedouins had found to the archbishop. Would he examine them?

Archbishop Samuel recognized immediately that the scroll was written not in Syrian, but in Hebrew. He broke off a small piece and burned it. He could tell by the odor that it was written on either leather or parchment. Whether it was genuinely old or a forgery he could not tell, but he decided to buy it. Later he brought three similar scrolls which the Bedouins brought him.

And now, realizing that scrolls like these could be sold for money, the Bedouins began searching the cliffs for more. They found several, which they sold through a middleman to a professor at the Hebrew University. But no one up to this time knew what the scrolls were, whether they were really old or not, or how they had got into the caves where they were found.

However, since there was a chance that they might have some archaeological interest, the directors of the Hebrew

University decided to send them to some noted scholars, and one after another the scholars pronounced them worthless. The matter might have rested there, but two professors at the American School of Oriental Research in Jerusalem were sufficiently interested to go a step further. They observed that the Hebrew letters of the scrolls were in an archaic form that had been used a century before the birth of Christ. With some difficulty they unrolled some of the scrolls, had them photographed, and sent the pictures to Dr. William F. Albright at Johns Hopkins University, in Baltimore, an eminent authority on Hebrew script. Dr. Albright thought them "an absolutely incredible find," and further investigation proved him right. Carbon-14 dating reckoned them to be about two thousand years old: a hundred years older than any Hebrew document hitherto known.

But who had written them? Why had they been hidden so strangely in these remote caves? Would a search bring forth more scrolls? What could archaeologists discover by examining the caves where they had been found?

Many people had begun to ask those questions now. The Bedouins were eager to scour the cliffs for more scrolls that they might exchange for money. And archaeologists wanted to inspect the sites where scrolls had already been found in the hope that they might find clues to their authorship.

Unfortunately all these efforts were interrupted, however, for just at this time the United Nations established the new state of Israel. Now tensions between Arabs and Jews ran so high that the two peoples were at war with each other.

In spite of the hostilities, however, Father Roland de Vaux of Jerusalem's École Biblique et Archéologique Française did manage to visit the cave where the first scrolls had been discovered. He found it entirely empty. The Bedouins who had been there before him apparently had looted whatever it contained. In a final effort he decided to sift the debris on the cave's floor, and from it he recovered small bits and scraps of many manuscripts. This was exciting, but still he was no nearer to the solution of the problems that mystified him. Who had made these scrolls and hidden them away?

On a desolate plateau overlooking the Dead Sea, not far from the cave where the first scrolls had been found, stood the crumbling walls of an ancient ruin, the Khirbat Qumran. Father de Vaux thought it reasonable to suppose that there might be some connection between the men who had hidden the scrolls and the men who had built Qumran. He made a preliminary examination of the ruin but, finding nothing of special interest, abandoned it until 1951, when pressure from scholars forced further excavation. Then the men of his expedition had not worked long in the ruins when they were rewarded by finding fragments of clay jars like those in the caves. Here was a proof that there was some connection between the people who had hidden the scrolls and the people of Qumran.

The persistent Bedouins continued to peer into every crack and hole in the area. In 1952 once again they found two badly corroded copper rolls. In another cave they un-

covered the biggest find of all: the fragments of no less than four hundred scrolls — a whole library.

Gradually, as Father de Vaux continued to work, the life of the people who had built the crumbling walls seemed to grow animate again. This had probably been a monastic colony, a religious center, where a group of Jews called the Essenes had sought refuge from the world. On this lonely cliff a mile from the shore of the Dead Sea the little community had lived what must have been lives of complete seclusion, under the leadership of one they called the "Teacher of Righteousness." They gave all their property on entering Qumran into the keeping of one of their order, the "Custodian of the Property of the Many," and spent their days praying and singing hymns of thanksgiving, in studying the law and copying their scrolls, and so in awaiting the end the world, which they were sure was not far off.

The road to Khirbat Qumran climbs and twists uphill and comes at last to a series of buildings enclosed in a walled space and dominated by a tall fortress-like tower — proof that the Essenes were subject to attack from enemies on the plain below them. Inside the walls Father de Vaux found the remains of rooms where the members of the community had worked, studied, and worshiped.

The largest room was refectory, where only those who belonged to the order called "Purity of Many" were admitted. It had been used for communal meals, but also for religious meetings, and here, too, they studied the law. For the Essenes interpreted literally the rule: "There shall not cease to be a man who expounds the Torah day and night continually to his fellow." At one end of this room was a raised platform, where one man stood to read the Torah.

Near the refectory was a kitchen, its plates neatly stacked, and nearby too was a kiln where the clay jars that held the scrolls were made and fired. Here the ashes still lay beneath the potter's oven, and several jars identical with those found in the caves remained as they had been when newly made two thousand years ago.

The building was two stories high, and the large room on the second floor was the scriptorium, where the scrolls were copied. The tables still stood as the scribes had left them, the inkpots conveniently placed. And on the tables also there were basins for holding water so that the scribes might wash their hands before they wrote the name of God.

The Essenes set great store by washing. Though there was no source of water on the desert-like plateau where their buildings were placed, they had built an elaborate water system to channel it from the green oasis of 'Ayn Fashkhah two miles to the south. The water was led from this spring to Qumran and held in numerous small pools and reservoirs, where it was used not only for washing and drinking but for the ritual baptisms which were an important part of the religious observance.

The ruined building at Qumran was not the only field for investigation in the area, however. Outside its walls to the east Father de Vaux found a large cemetery with about a thousand graves. Strangely enough, women and children were buried there, though none but men were admitted to the community at Qumran. Archaeologists think that the men of the order spent the night in huts or tents or in the caves of which there were so many in the hillsides, and they must have had families there.

That was the setting in which the Essenes lived and worked under their "Teacher of Righteousness" two thousand years ago. They came to Qumran late in the second century before Christ: coins picked up on the site establish the date. They must have stayed there about two hundred years. Archaeological evidence seems to show that they left for a time, perhaps when the great earthquake of 31 B.C. destroyed some of their buildings. But they returned, repaired and rebuilt their walls, and continued with their study of the law and their copying of the scrolls. Then in about 66 A.D. they left again, and this time they did not return.

That was the time when throughout Judea the Roman legions were bearing down hard on the Jewish people and the Jews finally rose in bloody revolt. No corner of the land was safe from violence, and even Qumran on its high plateau was not to be spared. It is easy to reconstruct what happened to the Essenes. When word came that the Roman soldiers were about to attack them, they took their treasured scrolls and hid them in the caves for safekeeping. They themselves must simply have disappeared into the wilderness.

And so the scrolls lay, unseen and forgotten, until Muhammed adh-Dhib came upon one of them when he sought his lost goat.

Today seekers have found the so-called Dead Sea Scrolls in eleven different caves, and they comprise as many as six hundred different works. The Bedouins are thought to have as many more in their possession. Some scholars believe that they may have $250,000 worth at the customary price of $18 a square inch, and there is some concern about how they will care for them. One Bedouin is said to have buried a bushel basket full of scrolls in the ground for safekeeping and to have found when he dug them up later that they were nothing but a gluey mass.

Still, scholars have enough to do for the present in trying to restore and to read the scrolls that have already been found. This work will take years, perhaps generations. Here are precious copies of every book of the Old Testament except the Book of Esther, but they are a thousand years older than the earliest copy of the Old Testament previously known to exist. There are also some parts of the Book of Genesis in Aramaic (which was the language Jesus spoke), a book of thanksgiving psalms, a work called "The War Between the Children of Light and the Children of Darkness," and a "Manual of Discipline" which was the rule of the order of the Essenes. The study of this last scroll was a help in interpreting the finds at Khirbat Qumran.

The study of the scrolls is considered so important that an international team of specialists from France, Poland, Germany, Great Britain, and the United States are now at work at the Palestine Museum under Said Bey Durra of Jordan's Department of Antiquities.

Millar Burrows in his book *The Dead Sea Scrolls* describes how this work is done:

The fragments must first be softened and placed between glass plates to flatten them. They must then be cleaned very carefully.... Some fragments are so brittle that they crumble even when touched with a soft camel's-hair brush. In some cases a light application of castor oil helps to bring out the writing but this too must be done with great care lest the material itself be discolored. Infra-red photography helps in many cases to bring out writing otherwise illegible. When flattened and cleaned, the fragments must be sorted out and, if possible, pieced together.

Once the scroll has been pieced together, scholars are then faced with the tedious and time-consuming task of deciphering each word in its context, work that might require days and years of patient study. Their task has been lightened, however, by the use of an electronic computer, devised by the International Business Machines Corporation and known as the "IBM 705." In Israel 29,245 words copied from the scrolls were placed on punched cards and shipped to New York. There the information was fed to the computer, which turned out alphabetical summary lists of the words at the rate of 150 words a minute. In this way all the major portions of the Dead Sea Scrolls which have been published have been completely indexed.

It is interesting to consider what the scribes at Qumran would have thought of this way of dealing with their precious scrolls, but twentieth-century scholars have hailed the

"705" as of incalculable importance. It not only will be of the greatest assistance in translating the ancient Hebrew texts, but also can make "qualified" guesses about words that have been lost in mutilated scrolls. The computer has replaced correctly as many as five consecutive words.

The discovery of the Dead Sea Scrolls with their ancient and precious Biblical texts has stirred new interest in the origins of the Old Testament and thrown new light on the life of the Essenes. Scholars in their quiet way rejoice because another page has been added to their understanding of the past.

15.

Great Zimbabwe

Now in the twentieth century by jeep and truck and airplane the archaeologists were moving farther afield. They were searching not only in Europe, America, and the Middle East, but in India, Siberia, China, and many other places. Africa, whose past had been little explored, drew many of them.

In the lonely jungle of southeastern Africa perhaps a hundred miles inland from the seaport of Sofala, there is a group of stone ruins called Great Zimbabwe. The word *zimba* in the Bantu language means houses, and *magbi*, which sounds like "babwe," means stones, but this is much more than a group of stone houses. There is a towering fort set on a hilltop and below it a skillfully built granite wall that encloses a roofless elliptical space. Two conical towers, one much larger than the other, rise from the wall near the ruins of what were apparently a great many stone dwellings. Great Zimbabwe is majestic, impressive, and altogether mysterious. Did a mighty king once dwell here with his court? Was this the center of some sacred cult? Who built it? And when? And why?

Throughout the middle ages no Europeans came to Great Zimbabwe. An American, Adam Renders, was the first to see it in modern times. He was hunting when he came upon those old vine-clad walls in 1868.

Renders paid little attention to what he had seen in the jungle. But a German geologist, Karl Mauch, who came upon them in 1872, was very much interested. He examined the great fort on the hill, the strange walls of the elliptical building, the conical towers, the arched doorways and stone staircases, and the ruins in the valley nearby. Mauch had seen many ruins scattered through Africa, but these had a grandeur and dignity that impressed him deeply.

As he walked among the ruins that were covered with jungle growth, Mauch could not believe that these structures had been built by native Africans. The Bantus, Negroes who lived in this area, built themselves huts of mud and thatch, and they had no tools or weapons save the most primitive. Surely a Bantu people could never have built structures like these.

One day Mauch went to talk with a mission priest who

worked among the Bantus not far away. There was a tribe called Lembkas who lived among the Bantus, the priest told him, and they practiced rites that seemed to be much like Jewish rites in a debased form. But how these Negro people who lived in remote southeastern Africa could possibly have learned Jewish rites the priest could not say.

The two men speculated and wondered for some time, and finally they worked out what they believed was a logical theory. King Solomon, who was so vastly rich, had got his gold from mines that were situated in what the Bible called the "Land of Ophir." Some had held that the land of Ophir was in Arabia, some that it was in India, or in far-off China. But Ophir might have been in Africa. The shafts of ancient gold mines had been found in these forests; perhaps it was here that the queen of Sheba lived. Perhaps when she returned from her famous visit to King Solomon she had brought back with her the knowledge of the ancient Jewish rites. Perhaps the fortress on the hill was a copy of Solomon's temple at Mount Moriah, and the mysterious elliptical building a copy of the building where the queen of Sheba had stayed in Jerusalem when she visited King Solomon .

Soon Mauch had persuaded himself completely that Great Zimbabwe was the capital of Ophir. He thought that King Solomon had had it built and that he had employed a Phoenician architect. There was a pattern carved in the stone over one of the archways that looked something like the pattern on an old Phoenician coin.

Karl Mauch did not live to elaborate his theories; he was

rather frail, and the climate of southeast Africa is hard on Europeans. But the theory that Great Zimbabwe was in the land of Ophir set fire to many imaginations. Bible students were excited at the thought that the famed land whose whereabouts had been unknown for so many generations was found at last, and those whose natures were more mercenary wondered if the gold of Ophir might not still be lying in the African ground. It was not long before a number of gold seekers were sailing down the African coast, landing at Sofala, and leaving their ships, to make their way into the jungle, where they were rewarded by finding many well-hidden ancient mine shafts.

One of the gold seekers who reached Great Zimbabwe in 1888 was a German named Posselt. He noticed as he approached the ruin that his Negro bearers were overawed by it. He said, "They sat down and solemnly saluted by clapping their hands."

Posselt could not enter the ruins by the main gate, for it was broken down, but he wrote, "We climbed onto the wall and walked along this until we reached the conical tower. The interior was covered with dense bush; tall trees towered above the undergrowth, and suspended from them were masses of 'monkey rope' by means of which we lowered ourselves and entered the ruins. I could not find any trace of human remains or of any implements, nor was the hope of discovering any treasure rewarded with success. Profound silence brooded over the scene."

No gold was to be found in the ruins of Great Zimbabwe,

but Posselt did not leave altogether empty-handed: he brought away with him two enormous stone birds. Perched on high pedestals of carved stone, their wings folded and their tall necks stretched straight up, these creatures are now on display at the National Museum of Southern Rhodesia.

Posselt's failure to find gold did not dampen the ardor of other gold seekers. They came now in great numbers. "To-day the Englishman is in the land of Ophir ... opening afresh the treasure house of antiquity," one English soldier wrote. In 1895 the Ancient Ruins Company was organized "to exploit all the ancient ruins south of the Zambesi River." They went about their work with great energy and reported that they had explored forty-three old ruins and recovered 500 ounces of gold jewelry, which they melted up to sell; the craftsmanship that went into making it was lost forever.

Many people were horrified at the work of the Ancient Ruins Company, for its members dug ruthlessly in their search for gold, destroying everything that came in their path. Cecil Rhodes, prime minister of the British Cape Colony in South Africa, disbanded the company after three years' destruction, and an ordinance to protect the ancient ruins was passed. But the ordinance came too late, for by that time immense damage had been done.

Then the British Archaeological Society sent David Randall-MacIver, an eminent Egyptologist, not to exploit the ruins, but to study them. And in scholarly but nonetheless heated phrases Randall-MacIver announced that the whole theory of an African Ophir was nonsense. Native Negroes had built Great Zimbabwe and the other ruined structures in Rhodesia as well, he maintained; there was nothing Jewish or Phoenician about them. He could not tell how or for what purpose the walls and towers had been used but he said, "Whether military or domestic, there is not a trace of Oriental or European style of any period whatever" in the buildings. He said, moreover, there was no evidence that any of them were more than a thousand years old.

King Solomon lived nearly three thousand years ago, so Randall-MacIver in his quiet way had demolished the whole theory of Ophir.

Still, if King Solomon had not built Great Zimbabwe, who had? The question was troublesome. Twenty-five years later the British Association sent another archaeological expedition to find out. This one was under the direction of the young archaeologist Dr. Gertrude Caton-Thompson.

Gertrude Caton-Thompson's findings agreed completely with those of Randall-MacIver. "Examination of all the existing evidence gathered from every quarter still can produce not one single item that is not in accordance with the claim of Bantu origin and medieval date," she said.

She established the approximate date of the building without too much difficulty. Diagonal shafts dug down beneath the walls unearthed pieces of Chinese pottery of a kind made in the ninth century, and further digging revealed innumerable beads. The tiny spheres and ovals of yellow, blue, and opaque green were exactly like those that were made in India and Indonesia in the ninth century. So the dwellers of Great Zimbabwe must have lived there in the ninth century, she concluded: they must have traded with the Far East. Carbon-14 tests made on a piece of tambookie wood recovered from beneath one of the archways confirmed the date.

Meantime Father Paul Schebasta, an Austrian missionary, working among the Bantu, had become interested in Great Zimbabwe. Since Portuguese explorers had just claimed this part of Africa, he thought he might find some record of it in Portugal. He went to Lisbon to see what he could find out from the library there, but the Portuguese had practically no records of this place, for they had not traded there; in the fifteenth century, their expeditions were headed for the New World. Father Schebasta therefore returned to Rhodesia to see what he could find out from the oral traditions of the Negro tribes that lived between the Zambesi and the Limpopo Rivers. He found out a great deal.

According to tradition there had been a rich and ancient kingdom that covered thousands of square miles in southeast Africa. It was called the kingdom of Manamatapa. Caravans, some with five thousand camels, had been sent from this kingdom as far as Timbuktu, to trade with the Arabs. But the king of Manamatapa also traded with the Far East, and merchants from India and China sailed down the coast of Africa and put in at the port of Sofala, bringing rich silks, spices, and jewels from India, and potteries and porcelains from China. The merchants, however, were not permitted to enter Great Zimbabwe where the king lived. They came near, laid their goods on the ground, and withdrew. Then the king's men came out of the forest and laid down what gold they wished to offer in return.

The ruler of this kingdom was very rich, for he controlled all the gold mines, of which there were many in the forest. His person was sacred; he wore garments of finest silk and on his head and on his chest ornaments of large sea shells. Whenever he went out drums were carried before him as if they were national flags. One of these drums was horrible, for in it rattled the bones of a human hand, the hand of a sacrificial victim.

The king had a large and numerous court and many wives. He had a chief steward, a keeper of the drums, a keeper of salves and medicines, and many pages who were the sons of tribal chieftains. Court ritual was highly developed and etiquette strictly observed. Whatever the king did was imitated by the members of his court. If he hurt his foot and had to limp, all the court limped. If he sneezed, all the court sneezed; if he laughed, the whole court resounded with laughter.

The king was constantly accompanied by his bodyguard, and the men of the bodyguard would eventually be his executioners. For, though he was deeply venerated by his subjects and his person was considered sacred, nevertheless when the time came for his successor to take office, he was killed. The murder of the sacred king was a holy ritual.

The people of Great Zimbabwe believed in life after death. Therefore when they killed the king they sacrificed many others with him so that they might continue to serve him.

Not only his servants and members of his retinue were killed, but a great many of the women who had been his wives. Their bodies were placed close to his.

The Bantu tribes, Father Schebasta discovered, believed that the ghosts of all their murdered kings are still at Great Zimbabwe watching over the mines that they controlled when they were living. Therefore even today members of the tribes approach the ruins cautiously. They are reluctant to lead strangers to it, and will not go there at all after dark.

It is only in very recent times that the mystery of Great Zimbabwe has been solved to some extent by investigation of oral tradition and archaeological methods. Father Paul Schebasta and Dr. Gertrude Caton-Thompson both arrived at similar conclusions, with the help of many other ethnologists and archaeologists. These ruins were not built for purely ritual use, nor were they purely dwellings; they were a combination of both. Round huts of wood and stone were once set between the closed walls of the elliptical building, and similar ones had stood in the strange gaps in the walls of the fort on the hill. But the main buildings were constructed without roofs, for these people were probably sun-worshipers who believed that the sun's rays must not be denied entry. It is thought that they may have been a part of the Eritrean cultural sphere, those sun-worshipers whose people lived not only along the coast of India but far out on the islands of Polynesia. According to legend, their first king had been the moon who wedded both the morning and the evening stars, and though his decendants still sleep within the lonely walls of

Great Zimbabwe they walk the earth too in the forms of the lion and the eagle. Great Zimbabwe in its immensity was not too grand a place for the seat of such a monarch as this, the Bantu believe.

There are some who still maintain that these walls could not have been built by native African people; that they must have been built by Europeans or under the direction of Europeans. Yet all the evidence seems to point to a native origin. Gertrude Caton-Thompson has written:

"The interest in Zimbabwe and the allied ruins should, on this account, to all educated people be enhanced a hundred-fold. It enriches, not impoverishes, our wonderment at the remarkable achievement: it cannot detract from their inherent majesty: for the mystery of Zimbabwe is the mystery which lies in the still pulsating heart of native Africa."

16.

Pictures in the Desert

The Sahara Desert covers more than 3,000,000 square miles, and scientists believe that once that land was green and fertile grassland. Once warm moist winds blew across it, nurturing its green luxuriance, and a wide-spreading river system drained fruitful shores. But that was a very long time ago, at the time when all Europe was covered with the great ice sheet, which influenced the climate of the countries south of it.

When the glacier receded, little-understood changes in the weather caused the soil of the Sahara to lose its moisture; then the vegetation died off, and pitiless winds blowing across the dry land stirred the earth into clouds of dust and blew it away. Now what had been grassland was desert, and almost all of the animals and men moved away, leaving it empty and still. They left no traces; no one knew how those men and animals had lived or where they had gone. Their existence was a mystery — until the French archaeologist Henri Lhote came to Paris in 1959 with a report of exciting discoveries.

All his life Henri Lhote had been fascinated by the Sahara. He had explored its most remote corners, had found a few stone axes and spearheads, and had examined occasional stone engravings. People must once have lived in that land, he knew, but what they were like, whence they had come, and whither they had gone he had no way of telling.

In 1933 Henri Lhote heard that a French officer named Brenans had come upon some rock paintings in a region called the Tassili n'Ajjar, which was in the desert in the southern part of Algeria. Lhote started at once to investigate, and when he saw them he was so filled with excitement that he lost no time in organizing an expedition to copy these extraordinary paintings.

Since the coming of World War II interfered with his plans, it was not until 1958 that he succeeded in organizing an expedition to study the paintings that had already been found and to search for more.

The Tassili region lies in the desert approximately 800 miles south of the Mediterranean. If you traveled to it from the north you would first traverse a wide stretch of billowing wind-blown sand, then cross a barren rock-strewn land, and come at last to the bleak sandstone plateau, which is the Tassili n'Ajjar. It is a strange place, seeming as empty of life as is the moon. Needle-like columns rise above the plateau's floor, grouped together like the tall buildings of a great city — a city that is deserted, empty, silent.

Making your way through these columns you come to a gorge overhung by cliffs and in that gorge there are passage-ways that were once the habitations of men. No men dwell here today, however; no one comes here except veiled nomads called "Taureg" who sometimes wander through that way.

The deserted cliffs and passages are peopled, however, not with human beings, but with thousands of painted fig-ures, all perfectly preserved in the dry desert air. Henri Lhote estimated that the most ancient was perhaps eight thousand years old.

Who were the artists who once painted here, and who the people whose images they put upon these walls? Where had they come from? There were no inscriptions of any kind, no writings that could tell the story of their movements. There were only hundreds of pictures in long succession on the rocky walls. But pictures sometimes tell as much as any written words.

The oldest of these pictures represent hunters, crudely painted in ocher, each one only a few inches high, with round heads that were too large in proportion to their bodies, Negroid features, and sticklike arms and legs. Many of the figures carried tridents that were much taller than they.

Perhaps the tridents were used for catching birds, but if this was the case the men must have been very skilled and agile.

Some of the figures in the most ancient paintings carried bows and arrows, for these hunters preyed upon wild oxen, which were also represented, along with occasional elephants and wild sheep.

As time passed and new generations of artists came to the Tassili the paintings became larger and more detailed, and several colors were used. These were earth colors — red, yellow, orange, brown, and blue-black. The arrangement of the figures was now more ambitious. Henri Lhote describes them as "archers struggling for the possession of flocks and herds, figures of warriors armed with clubs, of hunters chasing antelopes, of men in canoes hunting the hippopotamus." And there were dance scenes and people offering libations to some god. All the occupations of the people who swept across the Sahara in successive waves are pictured here.

Now there are people wearing jewelry, fine necklaces, bracelets and belts, and elaborate headdresses. Then it apparently became fashionable to have intricate designs painted on forehead, chest, abdomen, or thighs. One scene shows some men in an oval that seems to represent a hut made of mud and straw; it is shaped like the oblong huts in the Sudan today. And here are women at their cooking pots, men with axes about to split wood, children sleeping under a coverlet, and people sitting in a circle, talking.

Fascinating as all these pictures are, with their glimpses of life as it was lived so long ago, it was in their portrayal of animals that the painters excelled. After the generations of hunters had been replaced by herdsmen, cattle grazed on the green Saharan pastures. And now frequently the Tassili walls were covered with pictures of well-fed and strong cattle that moved in large herds. The beasts had lithe bodies and long curved horns. The artists who had been so observant of detail in representing human beings outdid themselves when they painted cattle. Probably no other people in all history have succeeded so well in catching the slow, easy movement of a grazing herd.

But cattle are not the only animals in these pictures, and this is the strange part of it. There are elephants, rhinoceroses, hippopotamuses, giraffes, gazelles, antelopes, lions, wild asses, and ostriches with balls tied to their feet — all these in what today is a bleak, rocky plateau where nothing grows. But giraffes live by eating the leaves of tall trees, elephants like to roam through tropical forests, rhinoceroses are accustomed to damp climates and wet places, and so are hippopotamuses. If those animals were once to be seen in the Sahara, it must have been warm and green there, with tall trees, running rivers, and green meadows. The guesses of those scientists who contended that the Sahara Desert had not always been a stretch of sand and rocks were suddenly confirmed by the finding of the Tassili pictures.

As the centuries passed, many generations of Negroid people succeeded one another; no one yet can say how many. And then newcomers invaded the Tassili. Probably they came driving their own cattle before them in search of fresh pastures, and what happened to the former inhabitants is not known. Perhaps those earlier settlers were driven to the south and east to mingle with the people who were already there, but this we cannot tell; the movements of the African aborigines will take a long time to trace.

At any rate, the newcomers to the Tassili made pictures of their own, and in them it is evident that they were not round-headed and Negroid like the earlier dwellers there. They had straight noses and looked more like Egyptian or Mediterranean people. Their pictures show goddesses with heads of birds like the goddesses of Egypt, and boats bearing standards of Egyptian provinces like those that sailed the waters of the upper Nile. And strangest of all were the chariots, their horses galloping with flying feet. Had horses once drawn chariots across the land that was now a desert? All these pictures seemed to prove that the people who had invaded the Tassili must either have come from Egypt and the East or have been in close communication with the Egyptians.

The ages passed. The climate changed, the earth grew dry and incapable of sustaining life, and the latest people, who had come from Egypt or elsewhere, disappeared. Now Arabs with their camel trains crossed the desert, but there were no longer any settled inhabitants on the plateau. And no more pictures were painted on the rock walls.

Still the question remains and the answer has not yet been found. Where had they gone, those men who made the Tassili pictures? What had become of them? Did they settle in other parts of Africa? Henri Lhote cannot say, for, though it is one of the tasks of the archaeologist to trace the movements of peoples, and though some day the various strains that make up the African people will be fully understood, this will take a long time.

Meantime, other archaeologists are working in Africa to discover her past. That she has had a great past, that her people have created great civilizations, there is no doubt, for ruins of many ancient cities on the African continent prove this. But these ruins still are largely unexplored.

No one knows, for example, what fine things lie awaiting discovery beneath the mounds and temple floors at Meroë, an ancient city in Kush on the upper reaches of the White Nile. It was the center of a great iron-mining industry, and heaps of slag lie all about its ruins. Broken bits of pottery and metal objects indicate that the people of Meroë traded with far-off India and China, but this fact too needs further proof.

Jebel Uri, in the hills of Darfur, 600 miles west of the Nile, must once have had a huge population; it seems to have been the largest city in all Africa. The remains of three walls encircle its stone palaces and streets with their multitudes of ruined dwellings. These too are awaiting investigation. So we still ask, who were the people who built Jebel Uri? Did caravans stop there on their way from the Nile Valley to Nigeria? And when did the city flourish?

There are further questions to be asked also concerning what is now Nigeria, whose people were so skilled in carving ivory and casting bronze that in recent years the museums of Europe and America have vied with each other in collecting their carvings. And the new Nigerian government, though it has little money, has spent a good many thousands of dollars in trying to buy these treasures back again.

In Nigeria, too, the city of Ife once flourished, but not much is known of it now. Recently two British art historians, Bernard Fagg and Frank Willet, picked up eighteen delicately carved figures there. One is a terra-cotta statuette of a king and queen walking with their arms interlocked; another, two gagged captives cast in bronze on a macehead; and a third, the dignified and beautiful head of an African queen. These remarkable and lifelike figures were brought to New York and exhibited in the Museum of Primitive Art, but little is known of their makers.

Yesterday the empire builders regarded the Africans as savages whose tribes had no history. Today the new, emerging African nations are beginning to regard their past with pride, though so much of their history has been lost in the slow passage of the years.

It now appears that the very cradle of mankind was in Africa. For in 1959 the noted British archaeologist Dr. Louis S. B. Leakey discovered in Tanganyika the fossil skull and shinbone that represent the remains of the earliest known man. Potassium-argon dating of the rock in which the fossils were embedded indicate that *Zinjanthropus*, which is the name Leakey gave to this prehistoric African, lived more than one and a half million years ago, at least a million years before Java Man.

No one yet has traced the movements of the hunters and herdsmen pictured on the Tassili walls; no one yet has unearthed the secrets that lie buried beneath the ruined African cities. When the archaeologists have succeeded in investigating these things, there will be bright new chapters in Africa's long history.

17.

The Lost Cities along the Indus River

Early in the twentieth century Rakhal Das Banerji, a Hindu archaeologist who was studying ancient Buddhist shrines along the Indus River, came upon one of these at Mohenjo-Daro. This is a place 140 miles northeast of Karachi in what is now Pakistan.

The Buddhist shrine had a central court with thirty monks' cells built round it and was undoubtedly an important find, but what impressed Banerji when he examined its walls was the material of which they were built. Most of the old buildings he had seen in this area were made of blocks of sun-dried mud; they crumbled when they were wet and therefore had to be built very thick. But the walls of this old monastery were made of bricks of another kind. These were small, like modern bricks, and they were apparently oven-baked so that they were impervious to water. Banerji wondered where the monks had got them. Then he dug down beneath the temple and found a wall built of this same kind of brick. Gradually he explored further, and realized that a whole city had once stood on this site. The Buddhists had taken its bricks to build their shrine. Coins found on the site indicated that the shrine was built in the fifth century.

In 1921, a little while before Banerji found the city beneath the Buddhist monastery, another Indian, Daya Ram Sahni, had begun to excavate some mounds at Harappa on a tributary of the Indus in southwestern Punjab. And he also found a city of whose existence no man had any remembrance. This city too was built of oven-baked brick.

Not long after the finding of these two cities Sir John Marshall, who was Director General of Archaeology in India, observed that Harappa and Mohenjo-Daro were so much alike in many respects that they must have shared a common culture. And on investigation this culture appeared to extend over an area as large as Egypt and the Mesopotamian valley together. Forty-two smaller towns were found along the banks of the Indus, although there was neither time nor money to explore them all. Full-scale excavations were carried on at Harappa and Mohenjo-Daro, however. One of the

most eminent archaeologists to study them was Professor
R. E. Mortimer Wheeler.

The archaeologists all agreed on why the cities had disappeared. The great river has flooded its banks periodically
since earliest times. When the floods came, layers of mud
were laid down over the houses and streets. After the waters
withdrew, the cities had been rebuilt on the same sites according to the same plans. Each time, no doubt, the citizens
believed that their levees were stronger and that their bricks
were better. In some places the houses had been built over
nine times.

Scientific dating places the oldest buildings at about 2500
B.C., the newest ones at perhaps 1500 B.C. Though it was
not very difficult to find out when the cities were built, it
was much harder to discover who had built them. For a long
time it was thought that an uncivilized tribe from the north
who spoke an Indo-European language had been the first
settlers here. But according to present evidence, these cities
were built long before this tribe invaded the Indus Valley.

Mohenjo-Daro is a smaller city than Harappa, but it is
better preserved. Both are rectangular in form and both have
streets that cross each other at right angles. Some of the
thoroughfares are 35 feet wide, wide enough for carts and
chariots to pass each other easily. In both cities the streets
are laid in such a way that the wind from the mountains
blows through them. They were not paved; the dust and
mud must have been ankle deep.

Most of the houses are two or three stories high, and some

roof tops measure as high as 35 feet above street level. Since the level of the street was rising continually with mud washed down from the mountains and with the litter of ashes, rubbish, and garbage thrown down from the houses, extra stories were placed on top of the original ones in many places and the ground floors abandoned.

The houses had no windows, though they sometimes had slits near the ceilings of the various rooms. Perhaps these were all that was necessary in this hot place, but the streets with their blank walls must have been dull to walk through. Even the front doors were set around on the side streets.

The houses were entered generally through a courtyard, and here the cooking was done. There were some bedrooms, but probably people generally slept on the flat roofs of the houses as they do in many Indian houses today.

One convenience that every house afforded was a bathroom, its water piped in from the Indus River. The bathrooms were generally placed on the street side of the house so that the waste water could be let out through a covered drain into a well-planned sewage system under the street. Though the people littered the street with rubbish and garbage, their sewerage was carefully drained. In many places the brick floors of these bathrooms were worn smooth by the bare feet of the people who used them.

Of the many buildings that have been uncovered at Mohenjo-Daro and Harappa, not a single one, strangely enough, has been identified as a temple, and what the religion of these people was can only be guessed. In almost every house, however, a small pottery figurine has been found. These little figures are nude except for a short flaring skirt, but they are adorned with a quantity of jewelry, and each has a curious and elaborate headdress. This headdress is fan-shaped, and on either side of it there is a small cup that has smoke stains inside it. The figurines are carefully finished in front but roughly made in back. They may have been hung in niches or on brackets on the walls, where oil or small pellets of incense were burned in the cups on either side of the head, so that the goddess would listen to the petitions of the worshiper. Scholars agree that this figure was undoubtedly the great earth goddess who was so widely worshiped in the Middle East.

A great many amulets bearing the figures of animals have also been found. Some amulets display a powerful bull with one horn; others, a tiger, a buffalo, a goat, a fish-eating crocodile, or a snake; some have several beasts merged into one. Whatever the significance of these amulets, they would seem to show that the people of Mohenjo-Daro and Harappa held animals in great veneration, as do the people of India today.

Though there were apparently no temples, both cities had very impressive public buildings for the people to use and enjoy. These were built on citadels that towered over the other buildings of the cities. Wide terraces with broad flights of steps that lay around the citadels might have been used for festival celebrations or grand processions. The buildings were rich and handsome in design. One of these was an imposing public bathhouse, whose generous pool was skillfully lined with smooth brick. Around the pool were numerous small rooms, and chambers for warm baths, massages, and rest.

Another large and handsome building on the citadel is thought to have been a school, though whether those who studied there were priests, or students of politics or of something else, no one can say. Finally, there were a huge assembly hall, with tall pillars reaching up to the ceiling, and a granary with a wide loading platform, to which the farmers from the outlying districts brought their grain to be loaded into an enormous silo.

These were the buildings the diggers uncovered as they penetrated the reddish dirt of the mounds along the Indus River. They walked along those dusty, unpaved streets where the wind still blew down from the mountains, they turned over the little clay figures of the earth goddess and examined the amulets with their pictures of strange animals. In one place they found a well with hundreds of broken cups scattered round it. The people must have thought it bad luck to drink out of the same cup twice, the diggers thought. But very little indeed was discovered about the people who had lived at Mohenjo-Daro and Harappa.

For such things as these do not tell how the people lived, what they thought five thousand years ago, what names those people bore, or what events transpired in those houses and those streets. The streets are still, the houses untenanted; no processions mount the stairways of the citadel; there are no swimmers in the bathing pool, no sacks of grain on the wide landing of the granary. There are a few skeletons there, but they are dry bones.

We could breathe life back into those dry bones and learn the secrets of the old walls, if only we could decipher their writing. A great many inscribed tablets have been found but no one yet has been able to read them. The writing seems to be partly pictograph, like the ancient Egyptian hieroglyphic writing. It seems also to be something like the writing of early Elam, but it has some of the characteristics of the Brahmi alphabet of India, and of the South Arabian alphabet, and it seems to be related somehow to the script of Easter Island. On all these points the scholars agree, but so far none of them has been able to decipher the writing.

The cities along the Indus River flourished for about a thousand years, but we do not know the history of these people. What their political or religious ideas were, what their alliances or their wars, we cannot say. Only one fact about their activities has been discovered. Some Danish archaeologists digging on the island of Bahrein off the coast of the Persian Gulf found evidence that they had traded with the Sumerians who lived in the Tigris-Euphrates Valley.

A thousand years passed while those people lived out their lives along the Indus River, and then, perhaps imperceptibly at first, the winds began to change their direction. The monsoon winds, which had brought the seasoned rains, were receding toward the east. Now, where there had been plentiful rainfall to water the farmers' fields, there was drought. The fields were dry; the land could no longer support the people. Victims of hunger, many weakened and died. The great civilization along the river dwindled.

Then it was easy for uncivilized newcomers from the north to enter the cities, pillaging and destroying. These early Aryans came in small bands at first, then in larger and larger numbers. They swooped down into the city streets, killing as they came. The city dwellers tried to flee — small groups of skeletons have been found in the streets as if the people had been trying to run away. With the advent of the Aryans the civilization of a thousand years was swept away.

The Aryans must have looked with astonishment at what they found. They must have marveled at the tall, well-built houses, for they themselves had been accustomed to living in tents. They must have wondered at the woven cloth, the jewelry, the children's toys, the cosmetics, the pottery. They must have allowed a few of the citizens to live so that they could learn from them the uses of these things. And gradually they settled down and slowly they built up a civilization of their own, commensurate with that they had destroyed.

18.

The Russians Explore
the Royal Scythian Tombs

The people of the Soviet Union have an immense interest in archaeology; expeditions are at work in almost every part of that vast country. Though few reports of their finds have filtered through to the Western world, there is one undertaking that is of extraordinary interest. This is the recent exploration of the Scythian tombs in southern Siberia.

We know from literary history that between the ninth and the fourth centuries B.C., the Scythians were both feared and admired; they ranged the steppes of western Asia on their swift horses, raiding empire after empire. They were especially feared by the Chinese, who tried to keep them back of the Great Wall, and were hated by the Assyrians and Persians, who found them both insolent and bold.

For five centuries the Scythians were lords of the Eurasian steppes, continually moving from place to place in search of new pastures for their flocks and herds. Their men journeyed on horseback, but their women were driven in horse-drawn wagons under felt canopies. And they lived on the produce of their flocks and herds: meat, milk and butter, and fermented mares' milk, which they called "kumiss." One tribe, called the Royal Scythians, was stupendously rich; they controlled inexhaustible stores of gold in the mines of the Altai Mountains. The precious metal was beaten into stamped gold plates and bands which were sewn on the clothing of both men and women. It was this gold that brought them to the attention of later generations of men, centuries after the sound of their horses' hoofs on the steppes had been quieted.

Peter the Great was Czar of Russia at the end of the seventeenth century. He was interested in archaeology, and he issued a famous "ukase," or proclamation, announcing that any object found beneath the surface of the Russian soil must be regarded as the property of the crown. He ruled so many thousands of acres of forest, farmland, and lonely steppes, however, that his ukase was almost impossible to enforce. In fact, it was disobeyed almost at once.

For hardly had he issued it when news reached Moscow that gold had been discovered in the Russian territory of Siberia. Part of this gold was in the natural state, but part was in the form of stamped gold ornaments. The discovery had been made by some prisoners who had been taken during the wars with Charles IX of Sweden and sent to Siberia.

The Swedish prisoners had wandered across Siberia in bands, sometimes as many as three hundred together, and they had found much gold in what were said to be the graves of Scythian chieftains. As they were not interested in the ornaments but in the worth of the gold itself, they had taken the wrought objects to a goldsmith to be melted.

A small amount of the treasure the Swedish prisoners found, however, was preserved, for a Dutch fur trader and diplomat named Nicholas Witsen, who was traveling through Siberia, managed to buy some of the gold ornaments and smuggled the collection out of Russia.

The Scythian gold Witsen brought to Holland disappeared without a trace when he died, but he left a book which he had written describing it. That book, published in Holland, fell into the hands of Peter the Great, and the Czar immediately sent an expedition of his own to Siberia. To his great satisfaction, the search was successful. The gold the Czar's men brought back is now one of the chief treasures of the Hermitage Museum in Leningrad, where it is called "The Siberian Gold Treasure of Peter the Great."

But not all the Scythian gold had yet been found. Soon a rich mine owner Nikita Demidov in the Ural Mountains found more of it. He sent it to the Czarina Catherine I to celebrate the birth of her son.

And then in the middle of the eighteenth century Alexis Melgunov, a Russian Army officer stationed in southern

Russia, became curious about a group of mounds, or so-called kurgans, had them investigated, and unearthed no less than 54 pounds of wrought gold. He sent it as a gift to the Empress Catherine II; it was valued at 100,000 rubles.

The kurgans that Melgunov had found were the first of many scattered across southern Russia. But, though the first one had yielded such rich treasure, grave robbers had apparently visited the ones uncovered later; no more gold was to be found in them.

Perhaps for this reason, or perhaps because Russia had so many difficulties that she had no energy left for archaeological exploration, interest in the Scythian tombs seemed to wane. Not until after the Russian Revolution of 1917 were more of them explored, and then little gold was unearthed. But at Pazyryk, near the Altai Mountains of Siberia, in 1927 and 1929, and again in 1947 and 1949, an astonishing series of excavations brought forth new knowledge about the Scythians that made the finders feel that gold was unimportant.

A great many kurgans were explored by the archaeologists the Soviet government sent out, but perhaps the most interesting of these was the one which they called "Kurgan 5." Here a tall cairn of stones covered a timber-lined pit. It was the custom when a chieftain was buried to pile stones on his grave as high as possible. Some of the cairns were 60 feet high. Underneath the piled-up stones at Kurgan 5 the Russians found the chieftain's burial chamber. Grave robbers had broken into the tomb, perhaps soon after it was made, and they had stolen all the gold ornaments. Heads had been cut off so that necklaces could be removed, and arms cut off so bracelets and rings could be taken. When the robbers left with their loot they had not troubled to seal up the tomb again. Water that seeped into the chamber had frozen and the contents of the chamber had been covered deep in ice. For more than twenty-four hundred years every object that the tomb contained had been perfectly preserved as if it had been stored in a kind of deep-freeze.

The embalmed and frozen bodies of a man and a woman lay in the tomb. With them were bowls full of food, tables, cushions, rich clothing, and elaborately decorated harnesses, as well as various weapons and some musical instruments.

In an adjoining chamber there were a number of horses and a chariot with four many-spoked wheels, which indicated the importance of the dead chieftain.

All these things were what might have been expected in the tomb of a powerful and important nomad; what the searchers found next was more unusual. There were the poles and framework of a tent and a flask of hemp seeds. Here was evidence that in their lives the tomb's inhabitants had indulged in the wild, visionary ecstasies of hemp smokers. And this equipment was buried with them so that they would not need to give up hemp smoking when they entered the other world.

Other kurgans perfectly preserved in ice were now uncovered. Some of the bodies buried in them had Mongolian traits, others the features of men from the Near East. Apparently the Scythians were a mixed race. They had had traffic with the people of both East and West, as the contents of the tombs now demonstrated. In one tomb a perfectly preserved Persian carpet, 6 by 6½ feet in measurement, lay as a saddle cloth on a dead horse. It had a pattern made with bands of flowers, of horses mounted and unmounted, and of grazing gazelles. Red, pale blue, greenish-yellow, and orange, its colors had not faded through the passing centuries. Archaeologists agreed that it was the oldest carpet in the world.

But if the Scythians had traded with the Persians, they had contact with the Chinese too. In one of the frozen tombs there was a beautiful Chinese textile. It was of silk, embroidered in a pattern of pheasants, some perched on flowering branches and others running among the bushes. Perhaps the lovely silk embroidery had been a gift from the Chinese emperor to a Scythian chief — there is no way of knowing. But it is certain that the nomadic Scythian must have treasured its delicacy and beauty, since it was kept among all the things he cared most for and could not part from, even in his death.

However, the Scythians did not depend on foreigners for all their textiles and trappings. They made saddle cloths and harness themselves. For these they used felt and leather, and sometimes they made patterns by sewing leather on felt in a kind of appliqué. One of their saddle cloths is a good example of this. It pictures a horseman with waving moustachios and a flying cape mounted on a lightly built horse. He has drawn rein and stopped before a bald-headed man in a long robe who is seated under a tree on an oddly shaped chair. (Generally the Scythians did not use chairs.) The horseman's hand is raised to his face as if he might be taking snuff, and the other man is clasping the tree trunk.

Is it the tree of life the bald-headed man is sitting under? And who are these two? Herodotus, the Greek traveler and historian, said that bald-headed Scythians seated beneath trees acted as judges. Is the man on horseback a law-breaker? What law of the steppes did he break so long ago?

Interesting and curious though works of this kind are, it was not in the representation of human beings that the Scythians excelled, but of animals. Horses, eagles, elk, deer, bears, panthers, and birds, as well as fanciful bird-griffins and lion-griffins, seemed to delight them. Animal designs are found on metal mirrors, sword hilts, bridle bits, and tent poles. But the most remarkable of these are the intricate and elaborate designs tattooed on the bodies in the frozen tombs.

The tattooed animals are naturalistic, yet they are accommodated to the arm or leg or thigh or abdomen they adorn, so that the whole pattern seems to be a wild fantasy. The tails of the animals are elongated and extend into flowering branches, antlers are divided into complicated curlicues, legs turn backward in violent, bewildering ways. The animal art of the Scythians was like an extravagant dream, its style unique.

This strange animal art must have been much admired by the other people of Eurasia. By the time the Roman Empire was breaking up and the Germanic tribes were pushing down over the Roman borders, Scythian art had influenced the Teutons very strongly. When they settled in Europe the Teutons brought with them some of the grotesque animal designs, for they too, according to the historian Livy, were accustomed to tattooing themselves. So in time the curiously distorted animals appeared again in the carvings on choir stalls, and in the queer gargoyles of the Gothic cathedrals, in the dragon heads of the Viking ships, and in coats of arms of European heraldry.

The world awaits the news of what other discoveries the vigorous Russian archaeologists have made, and meantime the Royal Scythians, who raced across the steppes on their swift horses so fast that it was said the grass never grew again where they had trod, are more real to us because those frozen kurgans have been explored.

19.

The Sleeping Dragon Wakes

A group of curious Chinese crowded into the Historical Museum in Peking one day in 1951. They had come to see an exhibition of murals reproduced from the walls of the famous Buddhist caves at Tunhwang in the far-off Kansu province. Several different artists had done the copying of these pictures, but chief among them were Chang Shu-hung and his daughter. The murals on which they had been working for some time displayed an array of ancient Chinese people. Here was an old battle, a hunting scene, some horses and carts, some dignitaries with their servants and musicians, all of whom had lived some fourteen hundred years ago.

The viewers looked with wonder and admiration at these

figures from China's ancient past. In fact, the exhibit created such a stir that two years later the government issued a new set of postage stamps decorated with motifs and border designs taken from the murals.

Not long after that another Peking exhibition attracted wide attention. This display was a set of photographs of the Buddhist cave shrines of P'ing-ling Ssu in Kansu, built probably about fourteen hundred years before. Although the shrines were definitely Chinese in style, the carvings had a strong Hindu influence which offended many of the viewers by its sensuousness. Nevertheless they were a reminder of China's ancient and proud past, and hundreds came to see them.

And again there was an exhibition of photographs taken at Mai-chi Shan, which the Chinese call "the paradise of woods and springs." Here 158 caves have been carved into the face of the rock cliff. In one section of the cliff is a huge recess with a canopy of carved stone over it. In this recess are seven caves and in these caves sit the Seven Buddhas of the Past, the last one being the historical Buddha, Shih-chia. There are murals here much like those at Tunhwang. One of them depicts a Buddhist heaven, with horses, musicians, and an elephant, all flying across the sky. Another shows a dignitary riding in a horse-drawn two-wheeled cart with his grooms and servants. The cart looks very much like the one in the Siberian Kurgan 5.

Strange though these carvings and murals might appear to Western eyes, they had great beauty and significance to the Chinese, who looked at them with deepest admiration. The Chinese people had always revered their ancestors; now they began to wonder who the gifted sculptors and artists were who had carved these images, and what life in those remote times had been like. The photographs and paintings were the seeds of a new interest in China — an interest in archaeology.

To carry on serious archaeological work it is generally necessary to dig in the earth, for the slow accumulation of dust through the ages blots out much that might otherwise be seen, and crumbling walls cover many of the things they once protected. But until very recently the Chinese had been unwilling to excavate the earth they considered sacred, because their ancestors had been buried in it. The graves are everywhere, for there were no cemeteries in China. When a grave was to be prepared the Taoist priests were consulted about the most favorable location for it. They observed the signs of wind and water, or moon and stars — and finally after much deliberation picked out the most auspicious place. So the tall, grass-covered cones of the graves are scattered everywhere throughout the country, each with its small opening so that the spirit could pass in and out. The people tended them carefully, placing little dishes of food to satisfy the spirit, who might otherwise come back to trouble the living.

Not long ago, when some foolhardy archaeologists tried to make an excavation, they were attacked by an angry mob and driven away. Railroad builders fared little better; they had to level the ground and lay their tracks under military protection.

All this was before the Communist revolution. Things are different in China now: the modern Chinese are eager to explore their past. For this purpose the Archaeological Institute of the Peking Academy of Sciences was founded in 1950, and since then the government has done everything in its power to further archaeological exploration.

There is a great deal of building going on in China today — the walls of new factories and new houses are rising in the the cities; new highways are stretching out across the country. Often in digging the foundations for these things old walls are uncovered, or old stones that have been carved or inscribed. Recently the government issued an order that when any such object is found work on the project must stop while an archaeologist is summoned to determine whether the site should have further exploration. Often the workmen grumble at this loss of working time, for the archaeologist must sometimes come from a long distance.

Still, by such painstaking practices as these, a great many interesting things are coming to light in China, and the people hail the finds enthusiastically. In 1954 and 1955, for example, a surprising collection of Christian relics turned up. They were found at Chuan-chow, which was a flourishing city when Kublai Khan ruled China in the thirteenth century.

Chuan-chow was completely destroyed at the time of China's war with Japan; its walls were pulled down and its buildings demolished. But some time later a Chinese school-

master came back to the place where the city had stood and
began sorting carved stones from the rubble. These he divided
into three separate piles according to the designs on them —
one group with Buddhist inscriptions, another with Mohammedan, and, in the third heap, gravestones that bore Christian symbols.

Wondering at the strange fact that there were Christian
symbols on these ancient Chinese stones, the schoolmaster
now consulted his history. It appeared that Kublai Khan's
mother was a Persian princess who was a member of a
Christian sect, and that the great Khan himself was much
interested in Christianity. In 1269 Kublai Khan had asked
the Pope at Rome to send a hundred Christian missionaries
to China. Only one came, and he did not arrive in Peking
until twenty-five years afterward. He was a Franciscan,
Brother John of Monte Corvino. Later seven others followed.

So there were a few Christian communities in China in
Kublai Khan's time, and one of these was at Chuan-chow,
where the schoolmaster had found the gravestones after the
Japanese demolition.

Each gravestone is marked with the Christian symbol of
the cross, but that cross appears in very unfamiliar style.
Sometimes it is mounted on a lotus flower, sometimes on a
cloud. On other stones the cross stands between two angels,
but not the kind of angels depicted in Western art — they are
angels with Mongolian faces, mustaches, and flying draper-
ies instead of wings. Some of them seem to be wearing trou-
sers and three-cornered caps.

The curious gravestones at Chuan-chow are only a small part of the evidence of the Chinese past that is now coming to light. For some time excavations were carried on at An-yang in Honan province, and in 1955 a report was made on these.

Modern Anyang is the site of the capital city of Pan Keng, an emperor of the Shang dynasty that ruled China during the second millennium before Christ. Pan Keng's capital was founded in 1300 B.C.

After Pan Keng had ruled at Anyang for some years, however, his astrologers advised him to move his capital from the south side to the north side of the Yellow River, and this he accordingly did. The new capital which the emperor built is buried now under the present walled city of Cheng-chow. This makes excavation extremely difficult. Fortunately, however, the ancient city that flourished three thousand years ago was a good deal larger than the modern one, and in the area around the walls of Chengchow the diggers went to work.

A potters' quarter was unearthed on one side of the city. Fourteen kilns were found, and there were potters' tools — clay stamps for decorating the surface of the pots with "ogre masks," coiling dragons, and other designs. There were also wooden bats used for beating smooth the outer surfaces of the hand-turned pottery.

On two sides of the city there were bronze-casting work-shops. The diggers found earthenware molds for casting bronze arrowheads and axes, as well as for ritual vessels, beakers, and cups. There was evidently a bone industry in this part of the city too, where awls, arrowheads, hairpins, and other things were made.

A royal tomb was uncovered outside the city of Cheng-chow. Grave robbers had long ago taken from it all that was of intrinsic value, and the body of the emperor was not to be found. But there were the skeletons of seventeen men on the east side and of twenty-four women on the west side, together with the bones of sixteen horses and some monkeys, dogs, and deer. Piled in the corners of the chamber, facing inward, were thirty-four human skulls. The thirty-four bodies to which these heads had once belonged lay buried in an orderly row outside.

It was strange that among all these gruesome surroundings there was a musical instrument. It was a musical stone, a percussion instrument of a kind still played in China in the ceremony commemorating Confucius' birthday. The ancient instrument is a slab of white marble with green mottling, about 1 inch thick, 33 inches long, and 16 inches wide. There is a hole in the marble so that the instrument can be hung from a frame while it is played, and one side of the stone is carved with a design of a tiger. This is the largest, and perhaps the most beautiful, of all the famous Chinese "singing stones," and it is more than three thousand years old.

Today the archaeologists, freed by public opinion from the fear of disturbing ancestors' graves, have made excavations in many parts of China. In Honan they found a chariot buried in a subterranean tomb large enough to hold not only

the chariot itself but the four horses who had drawn it. In Hopei they discovered the tomb of an emperor of the Han dynasty that contained a beautiful collection of wall paintings. The grave had been undisturbed since the second century A.D. There was another Han dynasty tomb in Shantung. When it was excavated, the Chinese who traveled out to see it beheld walls and columns all intricately carved in bas-relief, and those who were versed in the mythology of their country, as most of them were, recognized "The Scarlet Bird of the South Quarter," "The Somber Warrior," and "The Tortoise of the North."

Dwarfing these finds in magnificence, however, is the enormous imperial tomb northwest of Peking — the tomb of the Emperor Wan-Li, who ruled China from 1573 to 1620. Wan-Li's tomb is completely underground, and its contents, though very precious, had not been rifled by tomb robbers.

Massive double doors of white marble open upon Wan-Li's burial chamber. Inside the doors stood three massive thrones, their backs carved with a design of coiling dragons. In front of the thrones were incense-burners and candles in good condition, and three large oil lamps of blue porcelain decorated with a dragon design. The lamps were apparently intended to burn "eternally," for they were still half filled with oil. Perhaps the lack of oxygen in the tomb made them go out.

The emperor and his two empresses lay in state in red-lacquered coffins. The hair of the empresses, carefully dressed, was still in place, as was the reddish-brown mustache of the emperor. All three wore crowns of black and gold, but beside the emperor there was another crown. This was of gold filigree, bearing the golden figures of two dragons playing with a large pearl.

The tomb was packed with treasures. There were vases, bowls, coins, precious stones, gold, silver, porcelain, and brocade. Fourteen bolts of richly embroidered textile lay there uncut. The fabric was woven of silver and gold with designs of birds, flowers, rabbits, fish, and dragons. And there were countless objects of carved jade and of jade and gold beautifully wrought.

Close to the emperor's coffin lay his armor; his swords were encrusted with pearls and inlaid with jade. And a book written in delicate Chinese characters was there to describe the great deeds that he had done.

All these things were taken from the tomb and carried to Peking to be displayed in the Palace Museum there. And the Chinese people crowded to see them. For long they had not dared to investigate what lay beneath the surface of the earth; now they looked eagerly to see what had been there and waited for news of more discoveries. The sleeping dragon is awake.

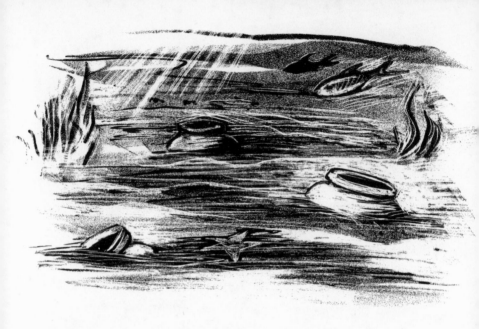

20.

The Search Goes under Water

Jacques Yves Cousteau, the famous skin diver and inventor of
the aqualung, is not an archaeologist. A thin, dark-eyed man,
a captain of the French Navy, he is fascinated with all that
lies at the bottom of the sea. In 1952, diving from his ship
Calypso into the depths of the Mediterranean a few miles
east of Marseilles, he came upon the wreck of an old Greek
cargo vessel. Professor Fernand Benoit, head of the Archaeological Museum at Marseilles, was with him at the time, and
so was Frederic Dumas, one of the finest divers of the French
Navy's Undersea Exploration Group. These men helped
Cousteau put together the clues they found bit by bit until

the whole story of the fateful voyage seemed to have happened not twenty-two hundred years ago but only yesterday.

In about 205 B.C. the Greek cargo ship, loaded with "amphorae," or tall jars, of wine, sailed westward through the Aegean Sea bound for Italy and the southern coast of France. She paused on her route at a port just north of Naples and took on a large shipment of dinnerware. Nicely designed and varnished with a smooth black glaze, the dishes had been especially made for the export trade.

The ship stopped once more on that voyage, this time near Rome. Here she took on more amphorae, each with a capacity of seven or eight gallons, and they were filled with the red wine of Latium. The hold of the ship was so full now that the jars had to be stacked in rows on the deck.

She was overloaded, her gunwales too close to the water, but she sailed on until she was within 10 miles of Massilia, which was the ancient name for Marseilles. Then she sank.

The rocky cliffs called Grand Congloué overhang the water in that place. Did she steer too close? Did a storm drive her against the rocks? Cousteau and his companions, coming there so many centuries later, had no way of knowing.

The ship sank upright and lodged among the great rocks on the sea's floor. Her anchor caught on a ledge but did not hinder her fall. After the waters had closed over her she lay quiet, undisturbed by the storms and swells on the sea's surface and the ships that passed back and forth above her. Her master and crew, lying on the sea's floor, knew nothing of the marching Roman legions or of the coming of Christianity, or the popes and kings of the Middle Ages, or the strong modern nations with their wars and revolutions. They knew nothing of the happenings in the world that moved above them as the slow years passed.

Gradually mud and silt covered the shipwreck, and sea worms gnawed the planks and timbers. Barnacles, sponges, and sea urchins attached themselves to the leaden plates that sheathed the deck. When Cousteau found the wreck, many of the amphorae the vessel had carried were empty; the Greek sailors apparently had pierced the seals of mortar and poured out the wine for their own use on the long voyage. After the wreck octopuses had come wriggling across the rocks and slipped inside the empty jars to make their nests, dragging in bits of stone, shells, and pebbles to protect the entrances.

During the passing centuries the mud and silt continued to fall. Pulverized limestone washed down from the overlying rocks, and the skeletons of millions of tiny sea creatures were deposited on the wreck until it was covered with a thick, heavy mass. Finally the deck fell in, and the amphorae and the pottery were pushed over the vessel's side into the water. In time, big boulders fell down on the wreck, but the impact was cushioned by the water so that no damage was done.

Gradually the ship was transformed into a great mound on the sea's floor — a tumulus with the necks of amphorae sticking up from it here and there.

That was what Jacques Cousteau found in the late summer of 1952 when he anchored his *Calypso* off the Grand Congloué. A professional diver had told him that a great number of lobsters were to be found among some amphorae that were scattered across the sea bottom in this place. Cousteau was not particularly interested in the lobsters, but he wondered why so many amphorae were there. He decided to dive down and see.

His first dive was a deep one. He went slanting past coral reefs and grottoes and saw the fish darting in and out among the fans of softly colored gorgonians. After he had reached a depth of 200 feet and found nothing more than these, he explored the ocean bottom. Then about 140 feet below the sea's surface he found the tumulus that had been the ship. At that moment the world's oldest seagoing ship ever found came back into the consciousness of men again.

When Cousteau surfaced and told Benoit and Dumas what he had seen, plans for exploring the wreck began at once. Fifteen expert divers were engaged, and soon the deck of the *Calypso* was a busy place, with men helping one another into the clumsy foam-rubber suits that would protect them from the cold sea water, and adjusting the tanks of compressed air they were to carry on their backs. When all these things had been carefully attended to, they disappeared into the water with a long leap and a flip of foot fins. A burst of silvery bubbles announced where each one of them had gone.

When they reached the wreck, the divers planned to pry loose with their hands the amphorae and other objects from

the tumulus. They would put these objects into a big salvage basket to be pulled to the surface when they signaled by jerking the rope. They would have to work very quickly. In seventeen minutes after they had left the deck the time-keeper on board the *Calypso* would shoot a rifle to warn them that they must surface again. For, even though an experienced diver can accustom himself to the pressure of the water, there is always the possibility that he will suffer from the dreaded sickness called the "bends." Staying under water too long can mean paralysis or death. A hundred and forty feet under the surface, where the wreck lay, the pressure was 77 pounds to the square inch; that is about five times the atmospheric pressure at sea level.

Knowing all this, the divers started to work. At first the objects came away from the mound without very much difficulty and the basket was filled quickly. But after the loose ones had been gathered the divers found that other objects stuck together as if they had been glued. Prying at a dish would sometimes shatter it to pieces, and pulling the handle of an amphora might break the jar in two. So now Cousteau decided to put down a suction pump; the divers called it a "bazooka."

The suction pump had a long tube about a foot in diameter; it was powered by an engine placed in a little house on the rocky cliff of Grand Congloué. It drew up mud and whatever was in the mud and dumped it into a big strainer, carefully placed in a position where the wastes would not muddy the water where the divers worked. There was some danger of breaking the objects that came rushing up through this hose and into the filter, but most of them came safely out of the foaming spout.

The diver directed the tube of the suction pump to the proper location. With a twist of a valve he turned on the compressed air, and, holding the "bazooka" nozzle with his right hand, worked around various objects to free them, then loaded them into the salvage basket with his left hand.

Hundreds of objects were brought to the surface with the help of the suction pump. The first dishes, cups, and bowls were encrusted with white fossils, but those that came from deeper in the tumulus were in good condition. There were hundreds of pieces of smooth black varnished ware and a great many amphorae. There were also stone cooking vessels that were covered with a smoky film. Cooking had apparently been done over a fire on the back deck, where the smoke would trail off in the vessel's wake. And there were a good many bronze fishhooks, which the sailors had probably used for fishing on the long trip.

As each object was taken from the salvage basket it was cleaned and carefully recorded in a book. The archaeologists estimated that the ship had carried fifteen thousand pieces of dinnerware and that the number of amphorae in her hold and on her deck may have been about ten thousand.

Cousteau had started his exploration of the wreck in the summer of 1952 and his men had continued to work at it all that winter despite rough weather. By spring it was evident that he needed more help. The American National Geographic Society came to his aid, providing both funds and expert assistance.

Now it was decided that a television camera would make it easier for the archaeologists to see what the divers were doing and to supervise the excavation. It was a great day when the expensive, specially constructed television set was dropped over the *Calypso*'s side.

It is dark at a depth of 140 feet: the sun gives only a diffused gray radiance. Therefore a 6000-watt electric bulb, designed for underwater use, was carried down to the tumulus. Such bulbs cost $90 apiece and burn for only an hour.

A party of officials and notables from Marseilles came to watch when the television was first installed. They sat in comfortable chairs in the *Calypso*'s cabin and watched the television screen while the powerful light flooded the sea's depths. They saw the graceful swaying gorgonians, the curious fish glimmering in and out, and the diver working at the tumulus with the suction pump — all this in a world that they had never seen before. After a while they began to shout greetings to the diver through a microphone, and were surprised somewhat when he seemed to hear them and waved at the camera. In the weeks that followed the archaeologists would use the television and microphone to good advantage in directing the work below the surface, but on the first day its function was simply to display a scene of overpowering beauty to a group of wondering French officials.

Day after day the quivering pipe of the suction pump brought up its foaming flood. And in time the stern of the cargo vessel was pretty thoroughly explored. The bow still lay untouched, however. Would a box of coins be found there perhaps? A bronze figurehead? It had been hoped that the vessel might be raised, and then whatever was there would be found. But sea water had rotted the wood, and sea worms had gnawed it; no planks and timbers could be brought to the surface intact, as they shriveled and crumbled when they reached the air. Had it not been for the fact that a thin sheathing of lead had covered the decks and the timbers, the outlines of the vessel would not have been discernible at all. Perhaps, the archaeologists thought, with careful measurements a replica of the ship could be made. Then not the ship itself but one exactly like it would reach the port for which she had sailed so long ago. Patiently, therefore, they began to obtain the measurements and draw their plans.

The vessel on which the divers worked had no name by which it could be identified. No log book told the story of the fateful voyage; even the owner's name was unknown. The only possible identifying marks were two symbols, either of which could be seen on the lips of those amphorae which were not too heavily encrusted with fossils. Some of them were marked 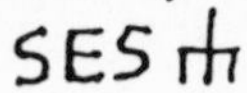 and some .

With these two symbols Professor Benoit went to Italy and began to search ancient records. After a while he came on the name of Marcus Sestius, a rich shipowner. Benoit studied the Roman historian Titus Livy and found that Sestius had left Rome in the third century B.C. and become a merchant trader on the Island of Delos in the Aegean Sea.

Delos, the city on the island that bore that name, was one of the richest cities of the ancient world. Because the Greeks considered it the birthplace of Apollo, many people came to the sacred city on pilgrimages. Ships from all over the Mediterranean crowded its harbor, for it was a free port. And traders grew rich there with human cargoes of slaves, as it was a center of the slave trade.

This was the city where Marcus Sestius had chosen a site on a street with a fine view of the blue Aegean. The town is nothing but a ruin now, for it was sacked by King Mithridates VI in 88 B.C., and twenty thousand of its inhabitants were massacred. Later the city was abandoned, grass grew up among the paving stones, the roofs of the houses fell in, and the columns of broken peristyles rose from the ruins like dismal tree trunks in a burned-over forest. It is an interesting place for archaeological work; the French School of Athens had excavated there for a good many years.

In 1953 Cousteau and his companions decided to pause long enough in their diving to sail to Delos in the *Calypso*. They found that the greater part of the city had been excavated, so that the streets and the walls of the houses were clearly discernible. Jean Marcadé, who was in charge of the work of restoration, offered to show them around. He took them past a splendid theater to a street that commanded a fine view of the harbor. Walking along this street, they came on the ruins of a fine villa. Here the pavement of the peristyle had been uncovered and the design, beautifully worked in mosaic tile, bore the symbol **S E S 卅**, the same mark they had found on the lips of a great many amphorae of the wrecked vessel. Another courtyard nearby had a design of a dolphin and an anchor like the one stamped on the lips of the other wine jars. Had Sestius lived in both these places?

"It would appear that the house was never finished," M. Marcadé said.

Was Marcus Sestius bankrupt after he had lost his great cargo ship off the Grand Congloué? Whether this was so or not, there was no doubt in the minds of Cousteau and his companions that they were standing in the very courtyard that had been built by Marcus Sestius, rich trader and owner of the vessel that now lay so quietly under the sea.

That was how the oldest Greek cargo vessel was found, but with the perfection of skin-diving techniques a great many more vessels are now being discovered. For the Greeks were great traders, and, though they prided themselves on their seamanship, many of their heavily laden freighters were lost on the treacherous reefs along the shores of the Mediterranean and the Black Sea. One diver, Peter Throckmorton, reported in 1960 that he had found the wrecks of no less than thirty-eight ships in two years' work off the coast of Turkey. The oldest of these has been identified as belonging to the Bronze Age. It sailed more than thirty-three hundred years ago, before Odysseus came home from the Trojan War across the "wine-dark sea."

So slowly the sea yields its secrets to archaeologists.

21.

Aviators Lend a Hand

In Europe the bombs of the Second World War were falling and the Allied generals were planning desperate and far-flung campaigns on land, at sea, and in the air. They needed accurate maps of enemy territory to show them where communication lines were located, where munitions plants had been built, where troops had been massed. The best way to get such maps was by aerial photography.

That was why John Martin of Oxford University in England was commissioned to fly over Italy. He was taking photographs of the terrain for the Royal Air Force.

Examining these photographs when he returned to England after the war was over, Martin found that many of them had a unique interest beyond that of an ordinary aerial survey. Not only could he see in them the towns, roads, railroad tracks, and farmers' fields of modern Italy, but also, strangely, as if he were looking at an X-ray photograph, he could detect the outlines of apparently man-made structures that lay beneath the earth. Here were what seemed to be the outlines of walls and houses and tombs built centuries ago and slowly covered by the earth and forgotten. The soil above the ruins had been plowed and planted, but still he could see where the buildings had been. It was like seeing their ghosts.

High in his airplane over the fields, he could tell where the old structures had stood by the way the crops grew. For the earth over the old walls was shallow and therefore drier than the surrounding soil, and where the soil was dry the crops were not so green or so tall. The photographs he had taken showed up the outlines of the buildings quite clearly. He could even see where the entrances to some of them had been.

Fascinated, John Martin went back to Italy after the war was over to take more of these revealing photographs. In the country that lay between Rome and Florence, up along the Italian coast and back toward the foothills of the Apennines, he flew over the little villages and their surrounding territory, pointing his camera down, taking hundreds of photographs.

This was the land in which the ancient Etruscans had

once lived. They had established their towns perhaps eight
hundred years before Christ and had built tombs like square
houses, not within the towns but on the outskirts. There were
literally thousands of such tombs clustered together like
little cities of the dead. Outside the little town of Tarquinia,
Martin took pictures of eight hundred leveled tumuli, and
near Cerveteri at least four hundred, while outside Monte
Abbatone he photographed six hundred more.

The idea of taking pictures of archaeological sites from
high in the air was by no means a new one. Back in the 1880s
cameras had been sent up in balloons and in box kites. During the First World War Colonel G. Beazeley of the R.A.F.
had taken photographs in Iraq of ruined cities that could not
be distinguished from the ground. Soon after the war, the
English began to make an air survey of all the archaeological
sites in the British Isles. So John Martin's enterprise was by
no means original, but he found what no one had discovered before. He flew over the little towns of what had
been Etruria, taking photographs of walls and buildings that
had long since disappeared.

The origin of the people who had built the ancient towns
he flew over was a mystery. They had left no literary sources
that revealed their history. Some records had been found,
written in an ancient Greek alphabet, but the Etruscan language remained an enigma, although some of the words had
been deciphered.

There was hardly any historical writing about the Etruscans by other peoples, either. Herodotus, the Greek historian,

said they had come originally from Lydia in Asia Minor but had left their country because of a severe drought and had "come down to Smyrna and built ships, whereon they set all their goods that could be carried on shipboard and sailed away to seek a livelihood and a country; till at last after sojourning with many nations in turn they came to [Italy] . . . where they founded cities."

"They no longer call themselves Lydian," said Herodotus, "but Tyrrhenians, after the name of the king's son who led them thither."

The name Tyrrhenian remains and is familiar in the "Tyrrhenian Sea," but gradually the Etruscans themselves were forgotten. Many people doubted that Herodotus knew who they were or where they came from, for his reliability as an historian has often been questioned. Moreover, Dionysius of Halicarnassus, who lived in Rome during the first century B.C., maintained that the Etruscans were natives of Tuscany.

Tradition said that the Etruscans had conquered Rome and ruled it as kings, that they had built the Roman Forum, and that, since the ground was swampy, they had constructed the great central sewer of Rome, the "Cloaca Maxima," which still drains into the Tiber. Tradition said that they brought the Romans their symbol of power, the ax surrounded by the bundle of rods which the Romans called the "fasces," and that they taught them to foretell the future by the cackling of geese, the flashing of lightning, and the examination of a sheep's liver.

But all these stories originated long ago, and they were

nothing but tradition. There was little hope of answering many questions about the Etruscans until after the Second World War, when John Martin flew over Italy taking his photographs. He took pictures at Vetulonia and Tarquinia, on the seacoast, at Volterra, which is within easy reach of the sea, and at the inland towns of Perusia, the modern Perugia, of Arretium, the modern Arezzo, and of Clusium, the modern Chiusi, whence Lars Porsena, the semilegendary Etruscan king of Macaulay's poem *Horatius at the Bridge*, is said to have come.

But when the photographs were taken, when the presence of hundreds of Etruscan tombs had been established — what then? Could the ghostly photographs be used to find out more about the people who had lived there so many centuries ago?

Recent research has lent support to the theory that the Etruscans first came to Italy by sea from Asia Minor and settled northwest of the Tiber late in the eighth century B.C. They were highly skilled metalworkers and exploited a number of iron deposits in Etruria. They excelled in bronze work, and their gold carvings are said to be finer than any in the ancient world. They were also vigorous traders. Their ships carried their metal products to the Greeks and other peoples of the Mediterranean region.

Besides being craftsmen and traders, the people of Etruria were good farmers. The fertile soil of Italy brought them great prosperity. Their crops of grain flourished in the Italian valleys, and it is thought that they brought trees and grape-

vines to Italy from the East. Most of the work on the Etruscan farms was done by members of neighboring tribes whom
they subdued.

By the sixth century B.C. the Etruscans ruled most of Italy.
Their civilization was at its height about 500 B.C. They loved
music, particularly the music of wind instruments; they
played at dice; and they engaged in horse racing: one of
their chariots is on exhibition at the Metropolitan Museum
of Art in New York City.

The Etruscans conquered the growing city of Rome in
about 600 B.C. and their kings ruled it for more than a century. After a long struggle the Romans managed to throw off
these foreign rulers, and in 396 B.C. they captured the Etruscan city of Veii. After that one Etruscan city after another
fell before the Romans and gradually the Etruscan civilization crumbled away.

The Etruscans appear to have had very little interest in
written records. Those that have been found are very brief
and no one has been able to read them. The language is not
Indo-European, but no one yet knows what it is.

However, though the inscriptions have not been read, a
great deal is being learned about Etruscan life through the
study of the tombs that are now being explored.

Several of these tombs, found and opened a number of
years ago, were known to be painted with scenes from Etruscan life. Some had marble sarcophagi, some furniture, weapons, and jewelry, as well-furnished tombs are wont to have
in many lands. However, after John Martin had made his

aerial photographs, it appeared that there were many more tombs than anyone had guessed. It would take years of work and thousands of dollars even to make a beginning. Many of them had probably been visited by grave robbers centuries ago; some might yield nothing of interest at all. The question was, where to begin?

Now the Italian industrialist Carlo M. Lerici devised a new, ingenious, and labor-saving way of finding out what was hidden inside the Etruscan tombs. He worked as if he were prospecting for ore. The first thing to do, he decided, after the aerial photographs had located the tomb, was to make an exact working plan for excavation. He did this by what is called "electrical resistivity soundings." All soil, he knew, resisted electrical current. If the soil is dry, the resistance is greater; if it is wet it is less. Now, therefore, he inserted steel probes on opposite sides of the tombs he wanted to excavate and passed electrical currents between them. The soil's resistance was recorded on a meter and this was transferred to a graph. When a sufficient number of these readings had been charted, the lines of buried walls and ditches could be plainly seen. In this way he found out where to dig with the least possible expenditure of labor. The vague outlines of the aerial photographs were transformed into an exact working plan.

But even with this accurate knowledge of where to dig, Lerici still had his problems. There were too many tombs. How could he tell which ones were worth exploring?

He found a way out of his difficulty by using another ingenious device, the "periscope camera." After he had found the exact center of a seemingly promising tomb by means of his electrical readings, he drilled a hole through the roof of the tomb chamber. Then he inserted a long hollow tube with a light and a tiny camera at its end. Rotating this tube slowly, he was able to take a series of twelve exposures which revealed the whole circumference of the chamber. In this way he found out what was inside without lifting a spadeful of dirt.

Some expense was involved in taking such a set of pictures, especially for so many hundreds of tombs. And there was necessarily some delay in having the films developed. Before long, therefore, an improvement on the periscope camera was made. This device, called the "Nistri periscope," has an eyepiece attached to the top of the turning tube, so that the archaeologist can look down into the tomb. Then he can decide whether it is worth while to photograph it.

So the work of investigating the Etruscan tombs began in earnest. One of the first and most interesting discoveries made in this way at Tarquinia in March 1958. Here the paintings on the walls revealed a group of athletes, running, leaping, dancing, and throwing the discus. In these frescoes the Etruscans appear as strong and lively as the contestants in the modern Olympic Games.

After that a number of lovely perfume bottles turned up. One was in the shape of a swimming duck whose tail served as the mouth of the bottle. And there was a magnificent big drinking cup with two handles which must have been used at some great feast, and a plate decorated with designs of sea life among which squids and sardines are easy to identify.

While the archaeologists were peering down through their periscopes and discovering these things, the aerial photography continued. And from the air it was possible to trace a system of roads that had joined one Etruscan town to another. These roads, wide enough for chariots, were built with drainage channels, tunnels, and bridges; the Romans, who prided themselves on fine road construction, had built nothing finer than these.

In 1954 the Italian government had undertaken a project to drain some marshlands near the delta of the Po River when some artifacts were unearthed at Spina. A little village existed there, but aerial photography now proved that it had once been a larger town, a town that was originally built up on piles above the swamp. The piles had rotted away with the passing of the years and the larger part of the town had consequently been submerged. Outside the town, the photographs showed, there had been a large cemetery, and, although it was under water and was known to have been visited by tomb robbers who were expert divers, there was much at Spina that was unexplored.

Excavating in the swamp posed a problem for the archaeologists. Sure that this site might prove a fruitful source, however, they probed the swamp in search of the roofs of the tombs. Wherever the rod struck a stone roof they decided to excavate. They surrounded the tomb with a light caisson of wood which would hold back the mud. Then a stream of water was directed at the tomb; the hose was more effective than any shoveling could have been.

So, splashing around through the mud, hammering away at their caissons, and directing their hoses carefully, lest the force of the water destroy some precious object that had so long been lost, the men investigated 180 tombs underneath the marshy ground. They found that a number of little tombs were grouped together in a special cemetery where children had been buried. The children had been laid here with their toys. Tiny breastplates had been placed near the little boys, and terra-cotta figurines of their dogs, while in the tombs of the little girls were small bronze mirrors, strings of beads and little bracelets, and nicely jointed terra-cotta dolls.

Nearby was a baby's grave; in this tomb the archaeologists found a rattle, a hollow terra-cotta ball with a loose pebble inside it. And here, looking further, they found, as in many of the children's tombs, the comforting figurine of the mother goddess.

It was long ago that strangers from the sea landed their ships along the coast of Italy, and built their cities there. The Etruscans apparently lived happily in that beautiful, fertile land. As the years passed they mingled and blended with the native population and gradually lost their characteristics as Etruscans. Who they were and where they came from are still unanswered questions. But the archaeologists of the twentieth century regard them gently now because of the children's tombs at Spina.

22.

The Search for the New World's Past

By the middle of the twentieth century there were few corners of the earth the archaeologists had not explored. They had carried on their long search in Europe and the Middle East, in Turkey, Iran, and Iraq, in Russia, India, and China. Africa, with its burning deserts and dense jungles, was proving a new challenge, and North and South America were beginning to tell their long-hidden tales.

The archaeologists now no longer worked alone in their searching; a great many different scientists lent them their skill and knowledge. Not only could the nuclear physicist tell them the age of objects they unearthed by the carbon-14 or the potassium-argon dating method, but the botanist also could determine dates by the examination of pollen or of tree rings. And the chemist could discover by his analyses whether a given bone or skull was a fossil or a fraud. The chemist also could treat newly unearthed and delicate objects so that they would not crumble away when exposed to the air. And cryptologists could read ancient inscriptions and documents that had long been undecipherable, for the ability to decipher codes and ciphers had been perfected during two world wars. In addition, electronic computers became available to help in reconstructing obliterated words or phrases in ancient documents. There were also the geologists, who stood ready to help with their new studies of the earth's structure, of volcanoes and the movements of glaciers; the oceanographers, who had new information about the tides and currents and the composition of sea water; and the geophysicists, whose instruments for detecting ore deposits could be used to decide which sites should be explored for tombs and buried cities.

With the aid of new scientific knowledge the archaeologist could be more certain of his conclusions now; his judgments could be more penetrating. And now he examines the site of his exploration from his position on the earth; and the aerial photographer shows him how it looks from the sky; and the skin diver, penetrating the ocean depths, brings him new objects to study from the deep sea. The present-day archaeologist is not a treasure hunter but a man trained in the scientific method who understands the relationship of many sciences to his own work.

A great many of these new archaeologists are working in North and South America now. With skill and imagination, they are using the most modern devices to investigate the American past. For there is a growing curiosity about the prehistory of the Western Hemisphere, and particularly about the past of the American Indians, who were the first inhabitants of these continents.

As a result of fairly recent research, it is known now that for many eons no human beings lived in the Western world. No men looked up at the snowy mountain peaks, or walked in the lush river valleys, or crossed the grassy plains. These places were the home of the mammoth, the elephant, and other animals that have since disappeared. Only the bones of these animals remain to be examined curiously by the paleontologists.

It is not known exactly when men came to this primeval world, but it is generally agreed that they came from Siberia. When the ice sheet receded in northern Europe, the reindeer herds changed their feeding grounds, and the men who lived by hunting the reindeer moved after them across Siberia. They came to the Bering Sea and crossed over it, probably in small groups that moved from one island to another. Some of them must have crossed on the ice; others probably came in little boats made of skins stretched over reeds. Since they were hunters they pushed down through the forests of Canada after game. Very slowly they moved down the West Coast and out across the continent toward the east, and into South America.

The journey took these first-comers thousands of years. Gradually small groups of the newcomers separated, adapting themselves to various places. Some of them stayed on the high plateaus of the southwest, and some followed the buffalo herds on the western plains. Still others hunted deer in the forests of the east and south. The most gifted tribes eventually built up the extraordinary culture of the Mayas, at whose ruins Stephens and Catherwood looked with such wonder a century ago; and very much later another group developed the remarkable Incan culture of Peru. Evidently the newcomers did not reach the tip of South America until about eight thousand years ago. A cave at the rim of an extinct volcano there gives evidence of their presence.

While a great many archaeologists are trying to follow the path of these first American travelers, others are concentrating on the past of the Alaskan Eskimos, about whom very little is known. They too came from Siberia, but they probably crossed the Bering Sea much later than the first immigrants. And, whereas the earlier dwellers in America were forest people who moved down along the coast toward the south and east, the Eskimos adapted themselves to the cold of the Alaskan climate, fishing in the icy water and hunting seals with their harpoons.

In trying to trace the long history of the Alaskan Eskimos Dr. J. L. Giddings of Brown University has recently worked out a new method of determining age called "beach-ridge dating," which depends on the action of the ocean along the Alaskan coast.

The new method was a boon to the archaeologists of the Arctic, for until very recently their task had been a most baffling one. At Kukulik on St. Lawrence Island in the northern Bering Sea they had found a mound containing an Eskimo dwelling which they thought might date back two thousand years. But when they dug into this mound, with its houses, caches of food, and burial places, they found that these had not been laid in neat layers as the diggers had hoped. Instead the Eskimos had dug subsurface floors in some places and pits for storage in others, so that new and old had been all jumbled together. The whole mound was a confusing conglomeration.

Ever since Heinrich Schliemann had dug into the mounds of Troy, it had been the practice of archaeologists to dig down through the strata of a mound to determine the various cultures of the people who had lived there. But stratigraphy of this kind was impossible at Kukulik; this mound was useless in tracing Eskimo history. And this was precisely why Dr. Giddings' "beach-ridge dating" was so important.

What were these beach ridges that Dr. Giddings now looked upon with so much interest? They were ribs of sand or gravel at the edge of the Bering Sea that had been thrown up by a severe storm or by the heaviest sea of a given year. Each ridge formed a wide, flat area on which people had lived or traveled back and forth without having to cross boggy tundra, mud banks, or rock slopes washed bare by beating waves. A ridge made an excellent place for building houses, for the frost left it early in the spring so that it was easy to dig foundations. Moreover, the ridge was close to the sea and the sea provided food — fish could be netted close to the shore and seals swam by in the deeper water. Boats for the seal hunts could be pulled up on the beach, and fish nets stretched out on racks to dry in the sun.

The beach ridges were useful not only for dwelling sites but because they made good communication lines. People could travel up and down the shore by boat in summer, and with dog sleds along the ridges in winter. The ridges were the highways that the ocean had supplied.

In the course of centuries the line of the shore changed; new ridges were cast up by the ocean. Then the Eskimos moved their dwellings, building on the new ridges that were closer to the ocean's edge, closer to the fish and the seals, closer to the beach road that made it possible for them to keep in touch with their neighbors. So, as the centuries passed, whole series of houses were built and then abandoned, and the deserted houses where such things as old stone lamps, cooking pots, flint tools, and harpoons were often left behind were gradually covered with blowing sand and forgotten.

It was in 1956 that the archaeologists first began to know the significance of the beach ridges. They realized that if they could find a succession of them, and if these contained structures and objects of different cultural periods, it would be possible to reconstruct the life of the ancient Eskimos, to read their history. The beach ridges might supply a chronology.

So in 1958 Dr. Giddings went hunting for such a series of ridges. He hired a skiff with an outboard motor from one of the Eskimos and started to explore 250 miles of coast line around Kotzebue Sound. He found that many beach ridges had been swept away by storms and currents, but at Cape Espenburg, on the south side of the sound, the coast looked more promising. Here fossil beaches lie in a succession parallel to the ridge that is now being formed. The beach nearest the coast is covered with blowing sand, but farther inland successive ridges, two miles apart, seemed to contain evidence of older and older cultures until at the farthest point the flints and other objects that Dr. Giddings found are the oldest known artifacts in Alaska: he estimated that they are no less than forty-five hundred years old.

At another place on the north side of Kotzebue Sound there was a spit made up of a dozen gravel ridges — a very good place for excavations, he judged. Remains of early villages were to be found on each beach ridge a mile back from the coast.

So the little skiff with its outboard motor made its way around the lonely shore of the bay, and Dr. Giddings found more and more sites that he thought might be explored. Soon the Eskimos became interested in what he was doing and began to help him. The man who owned the boat that he had rented told him of Cape Krusenstern, and Dr. Giddings went there. He found that more than a hundred beach ridges lay parallel to one another there, and every one of them appeared to contain ancient objects left behind by human beings. Cape Krusenstern gave evidence of human habitation that spanned five thousand years.

The work at Cape Krusenstern is just beginning. With the aid of aerial photography and all the devices that modern science can provide, the ridges that the ocean waves have left are slowly being read: the archaeologists are beginning to unravel the story of the Eskimos in the New World. And beach-ridge dating, which Dr. Giddings first used in Alaska, will be used on other coast lines in other parts of the world.

So the long search goes on. Methods have changed; new times have brought new ways of working. New tools and new devices have supplanted the old. But all round the world, in the earth, in the air, and under the sea, men and women keep searching. It is as if they focused giant spotlights that shine through the dark, now here, now there, to illuminate what time and the passing years have hidden away. The English archaeologist Geoffrey Bibby wrote, "Every archaeologist knows in his heart why he digs. He digs in pity and humility, that the dead may live again, and that what is past may not be lost forever."

Suggestions for Further Reading
Index

Suggestions for Further Reading

Bacon, Edward. *Digging for History*. New York: Day, 1961.
An account of archaeological discoveries throughout the world, from 1945 to 1959, made from articles first published in the *Illustrated London News*.

Baikie, James. *The Sea Kings of Crete*. New York: Macmillan, 1926.
The story of the people whose palaces Sir Arthur Evans discovered.

Bibby, Geoffrey. *The Testimony of the Spade*. New York: Knopf, 1956.
Extremely interesting accounts of Scandinavian archaeologists. Includes the finding of a Viking ship.

Burrows, Millar. *The Dead Sea Scrolls*. New York: Viking, 1955.
How the scrolls were found, and how scholars and archaeologists interpreted their meaning.

Carter, Howard. *The Tomb of Tutankhamen*. New York: Doran, 1927.
The story of one of the most spectacular finds in modern times.

Ceram, C. W. *The Secret of the Hittites: The Discovery of an Ancient Empire*. New York: Knopf, 1956.
Photographs and text throw light on a hitherto mysterious people. Translated from the German by Richard and Clara Winston.

Chubb, Mary. *Nefertiti Lived Here*. New York: Crowell, 1955.
A story written with great enthusiasm about work in Egypt.

_____. *City in the Sand*. New York: Crowell, 1957.
A brightly written informal account of work in Mesopotamia.

Coon, Carleton S. *The Seven Caves*. New York: Knopf, 1957.
The author goes from Afghanistan to Tangier to trace the

relics early man has left in caves. A book filled with adventure, with many lively anecdotes.

Cottrell, Leonard. *The Mountains of Pharaoh*. New York: Rinehart, 1956.
The history of the pyramids and their excavation. Good accounts of the Egyptologists, especially of Flinders Petrie.

———. *Lost Cities*. New York: Rinehart, 1957.
The ancient cities here described are chosen for their ability to excite wonder. The book is dramatic and entertaining.

Davidson, Basil. *The Lost Cities of Africa*. Boston: Little, Brown—Atlantic, 1959.
Africa and Africans south of the Sahara Desert before the colonial period: the work of scholars and archaeologists in the last twenty years.

De Laet, Sigfried J. *Archaeology and Its Problems*. New York: Macmillan, 1957.
Describes techniques and methods of modern archaeology including the new methods of dating. Translated from the French by Ruth Daniel.

Deuel, Leo (ed.) *The Treasures of Time*. New York: World Publishing, 1961.
Accounts of their discoveries written by archaeologists beginning with Layard in 1851 and coming down to the present.

Heyerdahl, Thor. *Aku-Aku: The Secret of Easter Island*. New York: Rand McNally, 1958.
An effort to solve the mystery of the great stone heads of Easter Island; by the author of *Kon-Tiki*.

Lloyd, Seton. *Foundations in the Dust*. Baltimore: Penguin, 1955.
The story of archaeological exploration in the Mesopotamian Valley. Includes the lives of Rich, Rawlinson, Layard, and many others. Very good reading.

Ludwig, Emil. *Schliemann: The Story of a Gold-Seeker*. Boston: Little, Brown, 1931.
Complete and interesting account of Schliemann's life and work. Translated from the German by D. F. Tait.

Morley, Sylvanus G. *The Ancient Maya* (third edition), ed. George W. Brainard. Stanford: Stanford University Press, 1956.

Sylvanus Morley was perhaps the first authority on the ancient Mayans. This is his account of their civilization.

Pallattino, Massimo. *Art of the Etruscans.* New York: Vanguard, 1955.
The book includes 126 very beautiful photographs by Martin Hürlimann.

Schreiber, Hermann and Georg. *Vanished Cities.* New York: Knopf, 1957.
This book contains vivid accounts of life in such cities as Babylon, Ophir, Troy, Mycenae, and the Ancient East. Translated from the German by Richard and Clara Winston.

Stephens, John Lloyd. *Incidents of Travel in Central America, Chiapas and Yucatán,* ed. Richard L. Predmore. New Brunswick: Rutgers University Press, 1956.
An 1841 classic that has not dulled with age.

Vaillant, G. C. *The Aztecs of Mexico.* Baltimore: Penguin, 1950.
A full and authoritative account of the people of Mexico before Columbus, their religion, arts, buildings, and daily life. Fully illustrated.

Von Hagen, Victor W. *Maya Explorer James Stephens, and the Lost Cities of Central America and Yucatán.* Norman: University of Oklahoma Press, 1954.
A very readable account of the adventures of Mr. Stephens and Mr. Catherwood.

Wilson, Edmund. *The Scrolls from the Dead Sea.* New York: Oxford University Press, 1955.
Edmund Wilson's articles on the Dead Sea Scrolls published in *The New Yorker* first stirred popular interest in them. This is a collection of those articles.

Wheeler, Sir Robert Eric Mortimer. *Still Digging.* New York: Dutton, 1956.
The autobiography of an archaeologist.

Woolley, Sir Charles Leonard. *Digging Up the Past.* Baltimore: Penguin, 1950.
An eminent English archaeologist tells how excavation has grown from a treasure hunt to a science. Based on a series of talks broadcast by the B.B.C.

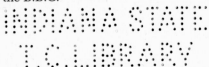

Index